Touchstones 1

A TEACHING ANTHOLOGY
Revised and expanded edition

MICHAEL AND PETER BENTON

Hodder & Stoughton
LONDON SYDNEY AUCKLAND

British Library Cataloguing in Publication Data

Touchstones: a teaching anthology.—
3rd ed. (rev. and expanded).
1. Children's poetry, English
I. Benton, Michael II. Benton, Peter
821'.008 PR1175.3

ISBN 0 340 39413 7

First published 1968
Second edition 1970
Third edition (revised and expanded) 1987
Sixth impression 1992

Printed in Great Britain for
Hodder and Stoughton Educational,
a division of Hodder and Stoughton Limited,
Mill Road, Dunton Green, Sevenoaks, Kent
by St Edmundsbury Press Limited,
Bury St Edmunds, Suffolk
Photoset by Rowland Phototypesetting Limited,
Bury St Edmunds, Suffolk

Contents

To the Teacher

Since the first *Touchstones* series was launched there have been major changes in teaching methods and many exciting new poets writing for children have emerged. We have revised the series so that the basic concept of the 'teaching anthology' remains. This is still the most effective way of combining three key features: an up-to-date selection of poems; teaching approaches which are primarily concerned with the individual's responses; and activities—often in pairs or small groups—which will bring the poems off the page. While many of the poems in the original volumes are retained, we have been able to include a generous selection of verse from current writers. The teaching sections on 'Exploring Poems' and the activities suggested at the end of each group of poems in the 'Anthology' have been completely revised and expanded. Even so, books can only do so much; poetry lessons, in particular, depend for their success upon a sympathetic relationship between teacher and pupils. When this exists children can learn more about what language is and what language does from experiencing poetry than from any other form of language use. What is more, approached creatively—with ample opportunities for performance and individual involvement—poetry lessons can be fun for both teacher and pupils.

The pattern of our 'teaching anthology' is as follows. First, in 'Exploring Poems' (Part A), we introduce three main topics which give information about a particular aspect of poetry, illustrate by examples and engage the children in talking, reading, and writing about poems. The individual teacher is the best judge of just how and when to use this area of the book. Secondly, in the 'Anthology' (Part B), we have grouped the material so that the teacher will be able to deal with several poems, linked by some common quality of technique, subject matter, style or attitude, in any one lesson or sequence of lessons. Thirdly, at the end of each section in the 'Anthology' we have provided suggestions for encouraging the pupils to respond to the poems in a variety of ways: live performances, tape-recordings, personal writing, displays and so on. We consider that pupils should be offered the chance to experiment, to play with the words, sounds and shapes of poems in the same way that they play with paints and materials in an art lesson. Unless it is developed, such freedom can become mere licence. Teachers, therefore, will often want to help children redraft their first ideas. Ideally, the 'play' element leads to a delight in the discipline of form.

Opportunities for this kind of personal involvement offer children both a means of understanding and ways of developing a 'feel' for poems which are not only enjoyable in themselves but also provide the best foundation for a fuller appreciation of poetry in later years.

Finally, we hope it is evident from the approaches we adopt that we do not wish the books to be followed slavishly as a 'course'. Indeed, the distinction between material suited, for example, to a second as opposed to a first form must sometimes be arbitrary. Although the books are numbered from one to five and the topics and poems have been chosen to suit particular age groups, teachers will find sufficient flexibility in the arrangement to be able to select and modify the material according to their own tastes and the abilities of their pupils. We also suggest the building up of resources to complement our selections. A mini-library of slim volumes of poetry chosen by author is essential in any school; and there are hundreds of practical ideas in the following books:

Michael Benton and Geoff Fox: *Teaching Literature 9–14*, OUP
Peter Benton : *Pupil, Teacher Poem*, Hodder & Stoughton
Sandy Brownjohn : *Does it Have to Rhyme?* Hodder & Stoughton
What Rhymes with Secret? Hodder & Stoughton
Ted Hughes : *Poetry in the Making*, Faber
Michael Rosen : *I See a Voice*, Hutchinson
Stephen Tunnicliffe : *Poetry Experience*, Methuen

PART A

Exploring Poems

WORD-PICTURES

Making a picture with words is often not so easy as it looks at first. We all think that we can describe things clearly and vividly enough —after all, we are doing it in conversation every day—but as soon as we try to describe something in writing the right words slip out of place and will not make the picture we want from them. It's difficult to give the shape of the idea in our heads the same 'shape' in words. Here are four ways of making word-pictures.

(i) Snapshots

A camera can take instant pictures of people, scenes, animals, or anything that catches your eye.

Your mind can take quick snapshots, too. As a class or in groups, try this: (make sure paper and pencils are handy first)

- close your eyes and concentrate on a single word—'rat', 'stars', 'rocks'—it's best to choose the *name* of something that will set going lots of associations.
- when the picture in your mind's eye is clear enough, open your eyes and take your snapshot by jotting down as many words and phrases as you can to describe what you see.
  Do this quickly; don't worry about spelling or making sentences for the moment. The time exposure for your notes is only two minutes!
- After two minutes are up, *in pairs* talk about your jottings:
  * Were there things you saw in your mind's eye that you couldn't find words for?
  * Can you and your partner add any words or phrases to each other's notes?
- Now, compose your picture.
  Arrange your notes, adding new words and crossing out ones you don't want, and try to make a two- or three-line snapshot. When the words are as you want them, write out a fair copy, checking your spelling and punctuation so that your picture is as clear as possible. (You could present each poem on a separate postcard to make a wall display.)

There is one sort of poem that is as brief and precise as these snapshots: it is called haiku and originally comes from Japan. As you will see from the following examples, haiku poems are only three lines long and, because of their shortness, they cannot include a lot of detail; they suggest more than they say. The haiku poet has to choose his words carefully because he is using so few. The poems may suggest a scene or incident, they may create an atmosphere, they may express a person's feelings, or they may do several of these things at the same time.

Here are two haiku* poems which create a picture:

Full Moon

Bright the full moon shines:
on the matting of the floor,
shadows of the pines.

KIKAKU

---

*All the Japanese haiku in this volume are translations by Harold G. Henderson in his book *An Introduction to Haiku* (Doubleday Anchor, NY).

Summer Night

A lightning flash:
between the forest trees
I have seen water.

SHIKI

As you see, these are clear, simple word-pictures in which the writer concentrates on one central object or scene and leaves the reader to fill in the details of the landscape from his own imagination.

What other details of the picture do you see in your 'mind's eye' when you read each of these poems?

In pairs or a small group describe the scene in each poem in your own words and see what details you add.

Notice how everyone makes a slightly different mental picture out of these few words on the page.

These haiku poems focus on two specific scenes. The first one does not explain which room the full moon is shining into, what sort of matting is on the floor, or what shapes the shadows are; nor does the second one tell us what sort of lightning flashed or whether a lake or river or the sea has been glimpsed through the trees. Instead, each poem *shows* us an instant snapshot, like the ones you have made.

If you want to take better photographs you cannot just point your camera and hope for the best. In the same way, if you want to make better word-pictures, snapshots are a start but soon you have to think a bit about composition. This is easy with haiku because the poems do not have to rhyme (even though some translated ones, like *Full Moon*, may rhyme the first and third lines). The basic form is a seventeen-syllable poem, the syllables being arranged 5, 7, 5 over three lines. Here are two regular haiku written by children of your own age.

Birds

A kingdom of birds, (5)
The voice of wings fluttering, (7)
A tune gathering. (5)

ANDREW

Poplar Trees

Green as the stream flows, (5)
Flickering whipcord in the wind, (7)
Lombardy thrashes. (5)

ELISABETH

Once you feel confident with your snapshots, try to write a regular haiku in this pattern. With a little practice you should find that you can come fairly close to the 5, 7, 5 pattern. In pairs or groups you could then try writing a haiku sequence of, say, four poems for the seasons of the year, or twelve poems to make a haiku 'yearbook' in which you catch the picture of January, February, March and so on. You may find, like Roger McGough, that haiku become a habit you cannot resist!

Two Haiku

only trouble with
Japanese haiku is that
You write one, and then

only seventeen
syllables later you want
to write another.

ROGER McGOUGH

(ii) Pictures of feelings

Word-pictures, like paintings or photographs, can also show feelings. They can be put together so that we focus on a single picture or event and yet, at the same time, we both see the scene in our mind's eye and know whether the writer feels joy, sadness, surprise or anything else about it. Here are three more haiku poems:

In the House

At the butterflies
the caged bird gazes, envying—
just watch its eyes!

ISSA

Parting

For me who go,
for you who stay—
two autumns.

BUSON

The Little Duck

'I've just come from a place
at the lake bottom!'—*that* is the look
on the little duck's face.

JOSO

What feelings do these poems suggest in addition to giving us a word-picture? What are the feelings of the caged bird? Why does the poet refer to its eyes?

In *Parting* what is the feeling expressed by the phrase 'two autumns'?

In the third poem *what* is the look on the duck's face? What does its supposed remark on surfacing tell us about how it feels?

One way to focus on pictures of feelings is to try 'list poems'. Everyone feels excited or bored, lonely or frightened at some time or other—as well as a host of other things as well. Take one feeling you have fairly often—loneliness, excitement, boredom, fear, and simply list five or six objects or scenes that you associate with it. Begin your list 'Loneliness is . . .', or 'Fear is . . .' and write down each phrase on a separate line. If several of the class have chosen the same feeling, you could get together in groups and combine the best bits of writing into a longer group poem to be illustrated and displayed.

(iii) Ways of seeing

The next poem is a list with a difference. First, read it through to yourself and you will see that it is a series of word-pictures of things that the wind does and does not do. Then in pairs, read it aloud, taking alternate verses.

Workings of the Wind

Wind doesn't always topple trees
and shake houses to pieces.

Wind plays
all over woods, with weighty ghosts
in swings in thousands,
swinging from every branch.

Wind doesn't always rattle windows
and push, push at walls.

Wind whistles
down cul-de-sacs and worries
dry leaves and old newspapers to leap
and curl like kite tails.

Wind doesn't always dry out
sweaty shirts and blouses.

Wind scatters
pollen dust of flowers, washes
people's and animals' faces
and combs out birds' feathers.

Wind doesn't always whip up waves
into white horses.

Wind shakes up
tree-shadows to dance on rivers,
to jig about on grass, and hanging
lantern light to play signalman.

Wind doesn't always run wild
kicking tinny dustbin lids.

Wind makes
leafy limbs bow to red roses
and bob up and down outside windows
and makes desk papers fly up indoors.

JAMES BERRY

Talk about what you see in your mind's eye from these ten pictures of the workings of the wind. Here are three ways of working on the poem:

* Copy out the poem carefully down the left-hand side of a sheet of plain paper and draw a series of framed miniature pictures alongside to illustrate each verse. Keep your drawings simple; perhaps concentrate on just a single detail each time.
* Can you and your partner add a pair of verses to the poem, describing other things the wind does and does not do?
* Or this poem may have made you think of the workings of the sun, or snow, or rain, or fog . . .
  Can you write a short companion poem in the same pattern? You might find it best to work in pairs.

(iv) A story in word-pictures

Here is a poem that might sound familiar. Do you recognise the patterns of questions and answers that go to make up the story? (There's a clue in the last verse.)

Read the poem aloud. A good way to do this is to have one person ask all the questions at the start of each verse and ten others to read the three-line replies of the apple, the pear, the marrow and so on.

Leaves

Who's killed the leaves?

Me, says the apple, I've killed them all.
Fat as a bomb or a cannonball
I've killed the leaves.

Who sees them drop?

Me, says the pear, they will leave me all bare
So all the people can point and stare.
I see them drop.

Who'll catch their blood?

Me, me, me, says the marrow, the marrow.
I'll get so rotund that they'll need a wheelbarrow.
I'll catch their blood.

Who'll make their shroud?
Me, says the swallow, there's just time enough
Before I must pack all my spools and be off.
I'll make their shroud.

Who'll dig their grave?
Me, says the river, with the power of the clouds
A brown deep grave I'll dig under my floods.
I'll dig their grave.

Who'll be their parson?
Me, says the Crow, for it is well-known
I study the bible right down to the bone.
I'll be their parson.

Who'll be chief mourner?
Me, says the wind, I will cry through the grass
The people will pale and go cold when I pass.
I'll be chief mourner.

Who'll carry the coffin?
Me, says the sunset, the whole world will weep
To see me lower it into the deep.
I'll carry the coffin.

Who'll sing a psalm?
Me, says the tractor, with my gear grinding glottle
I'll plough up the stubble and sing through my
throttle.
I'll sing the psalm.

Who'll toll the bell?
Me, says the robin, my song in October
Will tell the still gardens the leaves are over.
I'll toll the bell.

TED HUGHES

Each verse is a tiny word-picture—a bit like a haiku—only here the pictures are put together to tell an autumn story about the death and funeral of the leaves. Illustrate the poem either by

(a) drawing and colouring a series of ten pictures, one for each verse, which can be put up as a wall display; or by

(b) designing one large picture, perhaps a poster, which includes each of the things mentioned in the ten verses. Think carefully about the layout. Which figure is the most important? Is it better to make your picture tall and thin to catch the fall of the leaves from the tree to the grave, or to place the objects in a wide landscape?

Try to include as many of the words of the poem as possible in your illustration.

Take your mind for a walk! You can tell a story in word-pictures simply by finding words for the pictures in your mind's eye. As with the 'snapshots', make sure you have paper and pencil ready. Then:

- close your eyes and imagine yourself in a particular place you have visited recently—maybe on a day out or on holiday. Look about you, notice what you can see and hear, and be sure of where you are.
- When you have a clear picture picture of the place, take a mental walk and look at as many details as you can. Walk just a short time; two or three minutes are enough.
- When you have finished your walk, open your eyes and jot down in note form, in sequence, all that you can remember of your walk. Include not only what you saw, heard and touched but also any thoughts and feelings you had.
- Now, tell the story of your walk. Arrange your notes in groups of two or three lines each, each group focused on one detail. You can add other ideas as you want but keep the order of events the same. When you are satisfied with your poem you can write out and illustrate your fair copy.

COMPARISONS

(i) Two sorts of comparison

When we want to tell other people about things we have seen or done, or feelings we have had, we often use comparisons. We see a likeness between two things and decide to focus on that and for the time being forget any differences. Here are two haiku poems which use comparisons.

In the Moonlight

It looks like a man,
the scarecrow in the moonlit night—
and it is pitiful.

SHIKI

The Barleyfield

Up the barley rows,
stitching, stitching them together,
a butterfly goes.

SORA

The first poem makes a direct comparison: the scarecrow is like a man. The second poem *assumes* the comparison of the bobbing movement of the butterfly to be similar to the movement of someone stitching.

You may know these two types of comparison already as *simile* and *metaphor*. Both can make poems vivid and more exciting. They help poets to say more exactly what they mean, and they make both the poet and the reader use their imagination.

You can see how appropriate it is to describe poems like these, which are similar to sketches or drawings, as 'word-pictures'. In fact the haiku writer is doing in words what the artist is doing in the picture below, which is also Japanese in origin. Look at the details of the picture carefully.

What is the object behind the raised prow in the background of

the picture—a mountain or another wave?

What does the falling spray remind you of?

What does the foaming crest of the wave look like?

In answering these questions you will find that you have to try to think of comparisons. Now write a haiku of your own about this great wave in which you make use of one of these comparisons.

(ii) Look again

Comparisons help us to look at things in a fresh and original way. Writers often put two things together which we would not normally connect. D. H. Lawrence, for example, describes bats flying in the evening air as 'bits of umbrella'. Gareth Owen begins a poem about a waterfall like this:

'When the river threw itself off the cliff
It spun a twist of rope
So as not to lose touch with itself.'

Ted Hughes describes planet Earth in its orbit—

'With arms swinging, a tremendous skater
On the flimsy ice of space,
The earth leans into its curve—'

All these comparisons allow us to see the thing being described more clearly.

Read through the following ten comparisons. They are all extracts from longer poems, apart from *May Poem* which is complete*. As you read, give the words time to form a picture in your mind before you share your ideas in a group. It will be useful to make some jottings to help you remember this picture. Then ask yourselves:

- Which comparisons did you like?
- Which ones did you not *see* at all?
- Do you agree or disagree about what you saw and liked?

(1) Guy Fawkes

I am the caught, the cooked, the candled man
With flames for fingers and whose thin eyes fountain,
I send on the stiff air my shooting stare
And at my shoulder bear the burning mountain.

CHARLES CAUSLEY

(2) Waves breaking on the beach

Seen from above
The foam in the curving bay is a goose-quill
The feathers . . . unfeathers . . . itself.

LOUIS MACNEICE

(3) Sunflowers

Three astonished sunflowers
topping the garden wall.
frilled faces saucer-eyed
at being there.
giraffe-tall, gormless somehow,
heads hanging
over the next garden.

PHOEBE HESKETH

(4). A donkey

His face is what I like.
And his head, much too big for his body—a toy head,
A great, rabbit-eared, pantomime head,
And his friendly rabbit face,
His big, friendly, humorous eyes—which can turn wicked,
Long and devilish, when he lays his ears back.

But mostly he's comical—and that's what I like.
I like the joke he seems
Always just about to tell me. And the laugh,
The rusty, pump-house engine that cranks up laughter
From some long-ago, far-off, laughter-less desert—

The dry, hideous guffaw
That makes his great teeth nearly fall out.

TED HUGHES

(5) May Poem

rain falls

the candy-floss tree
rains confetti and
bridesmaids

pink snowdrifts
lie on the path

GERDA MAYER*

(6) Snowflakes

Snowflakes
like tiny
insects
drifting
down.

JOHN AGARD

(7) Boredom

Boredom
Is
Clouds
Black as old slate
Chucking rain straight
On our Housing Estate
All grey
Day long.

GARETH OWEN

(8) A butterfly's wings

On silent hinges
open-folds her wings
applauding hands.

MAY SWENSON

(9) Workmen retiling a roof

there are men
on the roof of the church,
playing patience,

tile after tile,

CRAIG RAINE

(10) Fawn

The spotted fawn
awoke to small leaf-netted suns
tattooing him with coins where he lay
beside his mother's warmth the first day

PHOEBE HESKETH

Most of these subjects are very ordinary—creatures, flowers, people working, moods; what makes them unusual are the comparisons. The writer has looked at something with fresh eyes, perhaps doodled around with the words and suddenly seen or slowly uncovered a likeness.

Try looking again at some familiar sights: a tower block of flats, winter trees, a pet animal, the shadows and outlines in your room at night-time . . . Choose your own subject and ask yourself what it reminds you of. Jot down one or two comparisons, talk about them with your neighbour, and then try to make a two- or three-line description from your notes.

(iii) What do you see?

Sometimes comparisons take over a whole poem so that, at first, you may not be able to see just what's going on. Read the next poem through slowly and ask yourself the questions afterwards. They will help you see what the tourist from Orbitville sees.

Southbound on the Freeway

A tourist came in from Orbitville,
parked in the air, and said:

The creatures of this star
are made of metal and glass.

Through the transparent parts
you can see their guts.

Their feet are round and roll
on diagrams—or long

measuring tapes—dark
with white lines.

They have four eyes.
The two in the back are red.

Sometimes you can see a
   five-eyed
one, with a red eye turning

on the top of his head.
He must be special—

the others respect him,
and go slow,

when he passes, winding
among them from behind.

They all hiss as they glide,
like inches, down the marked

tapes. Those soft shapes,
shadowy inside

the hard bodies—are they
their guts or their brains?

MAY SWENSON

CRAY

– What planet is the tourist looking at?
– What are the creatures that he sees?
– What is the 'special' creature that he notices?

Looking through the eyes of a visitor from outer space is one way of seeing everyday objects afresh. It's difficult to look at the world from someone else's point of view but it becomes easier if you think just about the objects a visitor would see. Let's try it. If, instead of a motorway, the tourist from Orbitville had seen a large railway station or an airport, how might he have described it? Work in pairs and see if you can develop one of these ideas. You can use the first two lines of May Swenson's poem if they help to get you started.

May Poem was first published in *Expression No. 7*, 1967.

BALLADS

(i) Ballads of all sorts

What are they?

You will know that a ballad is a popular song that tells a story. Ballads have a long history; they are very different from the tiny, tightly packed haiku poems which we looked at earlier. They sometimes tell their stories at great length. Several of the old Robin Hood ballads have more than ninety verses! These stories in verse were very popular with all sorts of people and many of them survive today as folk songs. Ballads have always had a strong connection with music. They were composed not simply as poems to be read but as songs to be sung or danced to or even worked to.

How were they made?

Although there were professional ballad makers and singers, the author of a ballad might be almost anyone—a farmer, an innkeeper, a shepherd, a tinker, a travelling pedlar—and he was probably not an author as we use the word for he would not write his story down. He would remember it and perhaps change the story very slightly each time he told it. New verses would be added, unsuccessful verses would drop out. People who heard the song would perhaps remember parts of it and add their own words to fill in the gaps. They might even add bits from a ballad they already knew and so a different version would be born.

What are they about?

There is an old saying 'the Devil has all the best tunes', and this is certainly true when we look at the subjects of the ballad makers. In mediaeval England there were still many who had a strong belief in magic, and women were frequently executed for practising witch-craft. Alongside the Christian religion the old pagan beliefs still flourished, particularly in the country areas, and many ballads reflect these beliefs. *The Unquiet Grave* (p. 48), like *The Demon Lover* that we look at in a minute, has a ghostly theme. A few ballads on

Christian subjects have been preserved into the present day as carols. *The Cherry Tree Carol* on p. 52 and *Mother and Maiden* on p. 53 are two of the best.

Work songs

People who work at repetitive tasks often sing to pass the time and to take their minds off the monotony of the job. This is as true today as it was in mediaeval England where such tasks as spinning and weaving, grinding and mowing, ploughing the fields and rocking the cradle were all part of the daily routine. An example of this kind of ballad is one which you may well know from when you were younger—*One Man Went to Mow*. Apart from these there are those ballad songs composed and sung by sailors to help them keep time in tasks such as hauling up the anchor and setting the sails. *Hanging Johnny* (p. 51) is a work ballad of this type. Do you know any others? What is the special name given to sailors' work songs?

Sensational stories

About 400 years ago a new kind of ballad developed. Booksellers and printers realised that these poems were very popular and soon ballads were printed and sold by the thousand in both town and country. Travelling pedlars and street ballad mongers, like the one in the picture on p. 26, made their living by them and, to sell more copies, they concentrated on crime, violence and scandal. For example, as late as 1849 the ballad of Rush's murder sold 2,500,000 copies. What was the new development that put such ballad mongers out of business?

Ballads today

Nowadays ballads are everywhere—from the pop charts to poetry books, from TV commercials to church services. Folk songs, work songs and carols continue to be written and sung; and poets continue to write ballad poems. One of these is Charles Causley and two of his ballads are on pp. 30 and 56–7. Changes in popular music this century have affected the ballad more than anything else. Whether you are interested in rock, modern folk songs, country and western or another sort of music, you will probably be able to find variations of the ballad. Look at one or two recent songs on record sleeves. Are they the same as or different from the lyrics of the more traditional ballads?

(ii) Performing a spooky ballad

The early ballad makers were the wandering minstrel and the harpist employed by a great lord. They would sing or recite their poems to a harp accompaniment emphasising dramatic points in their story by striking thrilling chords on the instrument. A favourite theme of the old ballad makers was the spirit returned from the dead. This happens in the next poem. Read it aloud in groups of three: you will need to prepare a reading with parts for the young wife, the spirit of her lover and the narrator. Make sure you understand what is happening in the story and decide carefully what tone of voice is needed at different points in the tale.

The Demon Lover

'O where have you been, my long, long love,
  This long seven years and more?'
'O I'm come to seek my former vows
  Ye granted me before.'

'O hold your tongue of your former vows,
  For they will breed sad strife;
O hold your tongue of your former vows
  For I am become a wife.'

He turned him right and round about,
  And the tear blinded his ee:
'I would never hae trodden on Irish ground,
  If it had not been for thee.

'I might hae had a king's daughter,
  Far, far beyond the sea;
I might have had a king's daughter,
  Had it not been for love o' thee.'

'If ye might have had a king's daughter,
  Yeself ye had to blame;
Ye might have taken the king's daughter,
  For ye kend* that I was nane.†

**knew †none*

'If I was to leave my husband dear,
   And my two babes also,
O what have you to take me to,
   If with you I should go?'

'I have seven ships upon the sea—
   And the eighth brought me to land—
With four-and-twenty bold mariners,
   And music on every hand.'

She has taken up her two little babes,
   Kissed them both cheek and chin:
'O fare ye well, my own two babes,
   For I'll never see you again.'

She set her foot upon the ship,
   No mariners could she behold;
But the sails were made of taffeta,
   And the masts of beaten gold.

She had not sailed a league, a league,
A league but barely three,
When dismal grew his countenance,
And drumlie* grew his ee.† *gloomy, murky †eye

They had not sailed a league, a league,
A league but barely three,
Until she espied his cloven foot,
And she wept right bitterly.

'O hold your tongue of your weeping,' says he,
'Of your weeping now let me be;
I will shew you how the lilies grow
On the banks of Italy.'

'O what hills are yon, yon pleasant hills,
That the sun shines sweetly on?'
'O yon are the hills of heaven,' he said,
'Where you will never win.'

'O whaten* a mountain is yon,' she said, *what sort of*
'All so dreary with frost and snow?'
'O yon is the mountain of hell,' he cried,
'Where you and I will go.'

He struck the top-mast with his hand,
The fore-mast with his knee,
And he broke that gallant ship in twain,
And sank her in the sea.

As you see, a ballad does not go in for long descriptions; it gives you the bare facts and leaves you to imagine the rest.

- What are the main turning points of this story?
- Were there any particular lines that stood out as you read the poem aloud, perhaps because of the sound of the words, or the picture they created in your mind's eye, or the twist they gave to the plot?

(iii) Making a ballad

There are many stories of death and disaster in the early ballads. One of the most dramatic of these is the story of *Sir Patrick Spens* on p. 46. Again, we are simply given an outline, not a lot of detail. What description there is helps the story along; the emphasis is upon the action. Notice how the story develops in a series of 'flashes', rather like a film cutting from one event to another:

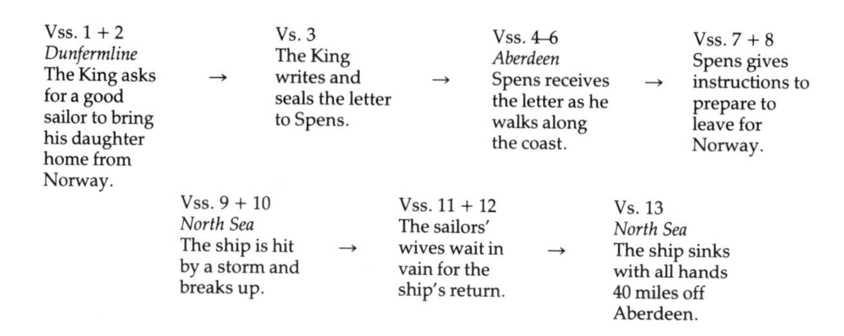

Writing a ballad is more difficult than making a haiku but try it and see how you get on. Here are a few simple guidelines and an example to help you. It is probably best to work in pairs.

* Agree on a story. Battles, disasters, ghosts are all common in older ballads, as we have seen. Traditional stories make good topics—the creation of the world in seven days, or Noah's ark, or Christmas or other festivals; but you can choose a more modern subject, as in the 'fight ballad' below, such as a football match, a race or a school trip.

* Work out a story-plan for about six verses, perhaps set out like the one above. Keep it simple. Make sure your story has a beginning, middle and end.

* Read through several ballads and listen particularly to the rhythms and rhymes. A common pattern is to have a four-line verse in which lines 1 and 3 are longer than the others and where lines 2 and 4 rhyme.

* Decide on the pattern that sounds best to you and write your first verse. If you get stuck, don't worry; leave a gap and try a later verse on your story-plan.

* When you finish your ballad, write out a fair copy and illustrate it boldly so that it can be put up on display.

Here is an example of a modern ballad written by a boy of thirteen. We have altered two or three lines slightly, just to smooth out the rhythm; otherwise, it's all his own work.

The Ballad of Bovver Pete

In a house
On Windblown Street,
Lived a boy
Called bovver Pete.

He wore big boots
Upon his feet,
A real tough nut
Was bovver Pete.

He'd go out all day
Walking tall,
And practise bovver
On a hard brick wall.

His head was hard,
As hard as brick,
He was very tough
But also thick.

Yes bovver Pete
Man he was tough,
But he met his match
In Jim Macduff.

Now bovver Pete
He picked a fight,
With Jim Macduff
One winter's night.

Now bovver Pete
He gave him nuts,
And quickly followed
With a few head-butts.

Now Jim got angry
Took out his blade,
And Pete now became
Just second-grade.

Now Pete he slowly
Backed away,
He wanted to live
Till another day.

But Jim struck quick
His knife felt blood,
And Pete did fall
In the filthy mud.

Now bovver Pete
He's gone up top,
To the skinhead club
And the bovver shop.

Now everyone will remember Pete,
And take off their hats and say:
He wasn't really all that bad
In his own sorta way.

EFSTATHIOS

(iv) Mystery story

Spooky stories, funny stories, mysterious stories . . .
The next poem is full of questions. We are not so much told a story—we have to piece it together from listening to the questions the child asks and the answers the mother gives. Listen to the poem read aloud, read it through for yourself, and then try to work out what might have happened to Lulu the night before. What is the state of mind of each of the three characters—the child who asks the questions, the mother and the missing Lulu?

What has Happened to Lulu?

What has happened to Lulu, mother?
  What has happened to Lu?
There's nothing in her bed but an old rag doll
  And by its side a shoe.

Why is her window wide, mother,
  The curtain flapping free,
And only a circle on the dusty shelf
  Where her money-box used to be?

Why do you turn your head, mother,
  And why do the tear-drops fall?
And why do you crumple that note on the fire
  And say it is nothing at all?

I woke to voices late last night,
  I heard an engine roar.
Why do you tell me the things I heard
  Were a dream and nothing more?

I heard somebody cry, mother,
  In anger or in pain,
But now I ask you why, mother,
  You say it was a gust of rain.

Why do you wander about as though
  You don't know what to do?
What has happened to Lulu, mother?
  What has happened to Lu?

CHARLES CAUSLEY

PART B

Anthology

Word-Pictures and Comparisons

Above the Dock

Above the quiet dock in midnight,
Tangled in the tall mast's corded height,
Hangs the moon. What seemed so far away
Is but a child's balloon, forgotten after play.

T. E. HULME

Coolness in Summer

In all this cool
is the moon also sleeping?
There, in the pool?

RYUSUI

Moon Magic

Leading me along,
my shadow goes back home
from looking at the moon.

SODO

Moon Viewing

The moon on the pine:
I keep hanging it—taking it off—
and gazing each time.

HOKUSHI

The Harvest Moon

Harvest moon:
around the pond I wander
and the night is gone.

BASHO

Dawn

Dawnlight opening:
on the barley leaf tips
the hoarfrost of spring.

ONITSURA

Haze

Morning haze:
as in a painting of a dream,
men go their ways.

BUSON

Heat

The summer river:
although there is a bridge, my horse
goes through the water.

SHIKI

Elephants in the Circus

Elephants in the circus
have aeons of weariness round their eyes.
Yet they sit up
and show vast bellies to the children.

D. H. LAWRENCE

Song

A widow bird sate mourning for her love
   Upon a wintry bough;
The frozen wind crept on above,
   The freezing stream below.

There was no leaf upon the forest bare,
   No flower upon the ground,
And little motion in the air
   Except the mill-wheel's sound.

P. B. SHELLEY

Crow

On a withered branch
a crow has settled—
autumn nightfall.

BASHO

Spring

They have the guise
of being married just today—
those two butterflies.

RYOTA

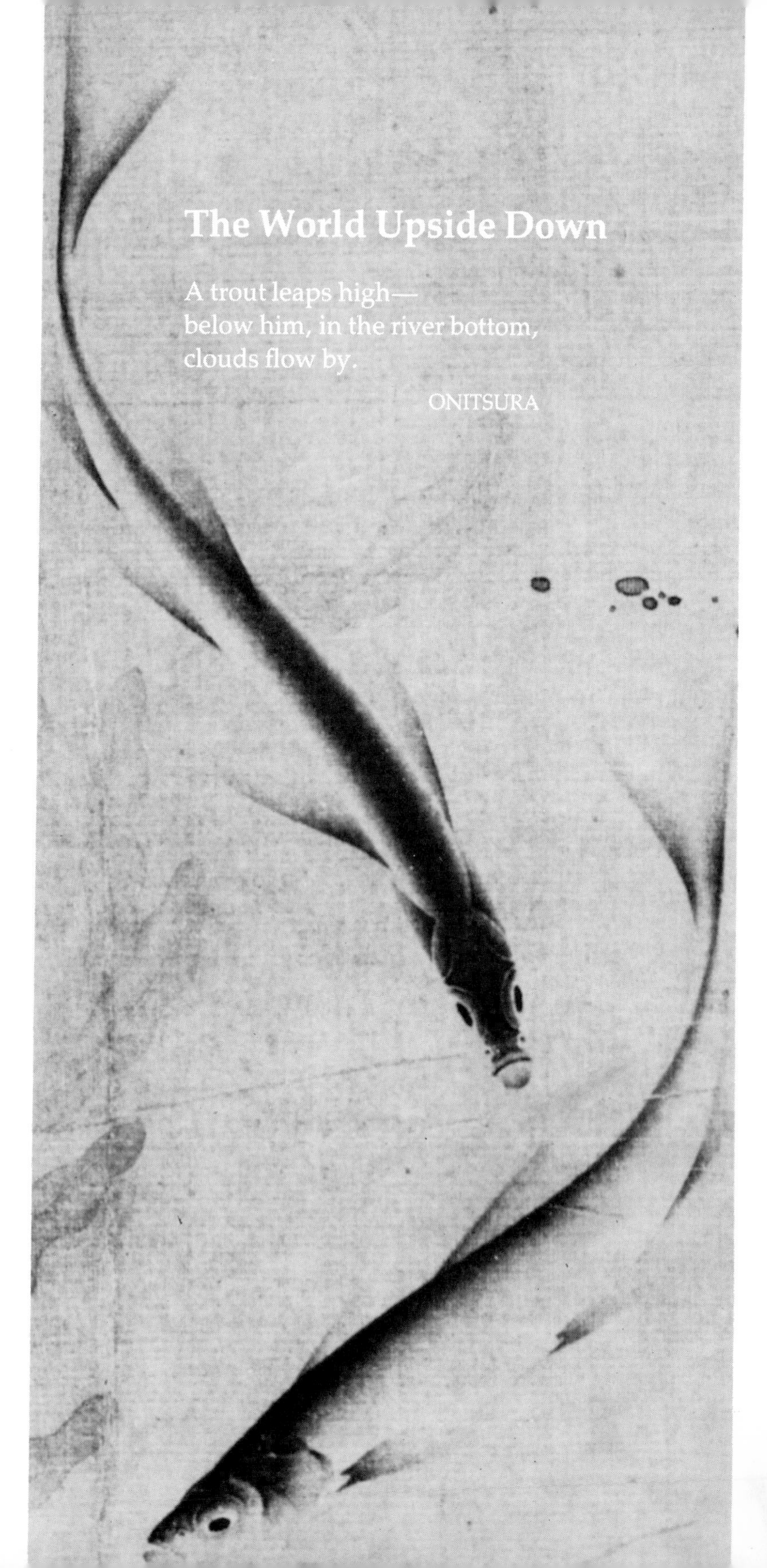

The World Upside Down

A trout leaps high—
below him, in the river bottom,
clouds flow by.

ONITSURA

The Fly

How large unto the tiny fly
  Must little things appear!—
A rosebud like a feather bed,
  Its prickle like a spear;

A dewdrop like a looking-glass,
  A hair like golden wire;
The smallest grain of mustard-seed
  As fierce as coals of fire;

A loaf of bread, a lofty hill;
  A wasp, a cruel leopard;
And specks of salt as bright to see
  As lambskins to a shepherd.

WALTER DE LA MARE

Winter

The winter trees like great sweep's brushes
Poke up from deep earth, black and bare,
Suddenly stir, and shake a crowd
Of sooty rooks into the air.

L. A. G. STRONG

Thaw

Over the land freckled with snow half-thawed
The speculating rooks at their nests cawed
And saw from elm-tops, delicate as flower of grass,
What we below could not see, winter pass.

EDWARD THOMAS

The Rainbow

Even the rainbow has a body
made of the drizzling rain
and is an architecture of glistening atoms
built up, built up.
yet you can't lay your hand on it,
nay, nor even your mind.

D. H. LAWRENCE

Talk

I wish people, when you sit near them,
wouldn't think it necessary to make conversation
and send thin draughts of words
blowing down your neck and your ears
and giving you a cold in your inside.

D. H. LAWRENCE

Spray

It is a wonder foam is so beautiful.
A wave bursts in anger on a rock, broken up
in wild white sibilant spray
and falls back, drawing in its breath with rage,
with frustration how beautiful!

D. H. LAWRENCE

The Fountains

Suddenly all the fountains in the park
Opened smoothly their umbrellas of water,
Yet there was none but me to miss or mark
Their peacock show, and so I moved away
Uneasily, like one who at play
Finds himself all alone, and will not stay.

W. R. RODGERS

Quiet

The night was so quiet
That the hum of the candle burning
Came to my ear,
A sound of breath drawn through a reed
Far off.

The night was so quiet
That the air in the room
Poised, waiting to crack
Like a straining
Stick.

The night was so quiet
That the blood and the flesh,
My visible self sunk in the chair,
Was a power-house giant, pulsing
Through the night.

RICHARD CHURCH

Listen

Silence is when you can hear things.
Listen:
The breathing of bees,
A moth's footfall,
Or the mist easing its way
Across the field,
The light shifting at dawn
Or the stars clicking into place
At evening.

JOHN COTTON

George and the Dragon

A boyish George, arrayed in gleaming plate,
lunges forward with lance and white rocking-horse.
The dragon's head dips in sympathy, bleeds
over the ground, on tousled patches of grass.

But she presents the beast with her palm out-
stretched as if a harmless pet pulled at the chain.
Is she deceived? Or is that fog behind
brave George, the black cave's echo, evil unseen?

MARTYN CRUCEFIX

Cinquains

TRIAD

These be
Three silent things:
The falling snow . . . the hour
Before the dawn . . . the mouth of one
Just dead.

NOVEMBER NIGHT

Listen . . .
With faint dry sound,
Like steps of passing ghosts,
The leaves, frost-crisped, break from the trees
And fall.

THE WARNING

Just now,
Out of the strange
Still dusk . . . as strange as still . . .
A white moth flew.
Why am I grown so cold?

ADELAIDE CRAPSEY

Autumn

A touch of cold in the autumn night—
I walked abroad,
And saw the ruddy moon lean over a hedge,
Like a red-faced farmer.
I did not stop to speak, but nodded,
And round about were the wistful stars
With white faces like town children.

T. E. HULME

Last Snow

Although the snow still lingers
Heaped on the ivy's blunt webbed fingers
And painting tree-trunks on one side,
Here is this sunlit ride
The fresh unchristened things appear,
Leaf, spathe and stem,
With crumbs of earth clinging to them
To show the way they came
But no flower yet to tell their name,
And one green spear
Stabbing a dead leaf from below
Kills winter at a blow.

ANDREW YOUNG

★ **Performance.** *Above the Dock, Song, The Fountains, Quiet, Listen* and *Cinquains* are all to do with different kinds of silence. Put together and read by different voices in a group, they would make a haunting tape-recording.

★ **Comparisons.** Jot down as many different comparisons as you can which are suggested by the following: clouds building up on the horizon; a snowflake; smoke billowing from chimneys; balloons —tethered or free; the back of your hand; soapsuds; raindrops on a window; frogspawn or tadpoles; frost on a window pane. Talk about these with your partner. Then choose one or two of your comparisons as the basis for making a short poem. If several of you have written good descriptions of, say, balloons, see if you can link them together into a longer poem, or 'tie' them together in a design.

★ **Haiku** (see pp. 4–6). Try to write some haiku of your own. Aim at variety. One haiku may be a simple picture; another may use a comparison; a third may express a feeling as well as give a picture. Use the following ideas if you wish: cranes; the world from space; a willow-tree; flames; loneliness; the cat; still water broken by throwing in a stone or by a fish surfacing; seagulls; the picture of the fish on p. 36.

★ **Viewpoints.** Write a poem that describes something from two different points of view. If it helps, you can begin the first part of the poem, 'Seen from above the . . . is like . . .' and the second part, 'When you get down it is . . .'. The following may help you:
- Compare a crowd in the street below with what it is like to be *in* the crowd.
- Describe the wake of a ship as you see it from a cliff-top or from a plane, and then as you think it would look close to.
- Above and below the clouds.
- Woods seen from above contrasted with what it is like to be walking through them.
- A train going through a valley seen from distance contrasted with what it is like when it passes very near you.

★ **Moon mural.** Work in pairs, either illustrating the five poems at the start of this section, or writing your own moon poem, or finding other moon poems to fit into a wall display.

Ballads and Stories

The Twa Corbies

As I was walking all alone,
I heard twa corbies making a moan:
The one unto the other say,
'Where shall we gang and dine today?'

'In behind yon auld fail* dyke *turf*
I wot there lies a new slain knight;
And nobody kens that he lies there,
But his hawk, his hound and his lady fair.

'His hound is to the hunting gane,
His hawk to fetch the wild fowl hame,
His lady's ta'en another mate,
So we may make our dinner sweet.

'Ye'll sit upon his white hause-bane* *collar-bone*
And I'll pike out his bonny blue een;
And with one lock of his golden hair
We'll theek* our nest when it grows bare. *line*

'Many a one for him makes moan,
But none shall ken where he is gone;
O'er his white bones when they are bare,
The wind shall blow for evermair.'

ANON.

Sir Patrick Spens

The king sits in Dunfermline town
  Drinking the blood-red wine:
'O where will I get a good sailor,
  To sail this ship of mine?'

Up and spake an elder knight,
  Sat at the king's right knee:
'Sir Patrick Spens is the best sailor
  That ever sailed the sea.'

The king has written a braid* letter *long*
  And sealed it with his hand.
And sent it to Sir Patrick Spens
  Was walking on the strand.

'To Noroway, to Noroway,
  To Noroway o'er the foam;
The king's own daughter of Noroway,
  'Tis thou must bring her home!'

The first line that Sir Patrick read
  A loud, loud laugh laughed he:
The next line that Sir Patrick read
  The tear blinded his ee.* *eye*

'O who is this has done this deed,
  This ill deed unto me;
To send me out this time o' the year
  To sail upon the sea?

'Make haste, make haste, my merry men all,
  Our good ship sails the morn.'
'O say not so, my master dear,
  For I fear a deadly storm.

'I saw the new moon late yestere'en
With the old moon in her arm;
And if we go to sea, master,
I fear we'll come to harm.'

They had not sailed a league, a league,
A league, but barely three,
When the sky grew dark, the wind blew loud,
And angry grew the sea.

The anchor broke, the topmast split,
'Twas such a deadly storm.
The waves came over the broken ship
Till all her sides were torn.

O long, long may the ladies sit
With their fans into their hand,
Or ere they see Sir Patrick Spens
Come sailing to the strand.

O long, long may the maidens stand
With their gold combs in their hair,
Before they'll see their own dear loves
Come home to greet them there.

O forty miles off Aberdeen
'Tis fifty fathom deep.
And there lies good Sir Patrick Spens
With the Scots lords at his feet.

ANON.

The Unquiet Grave

'The wind doth blow today, my love,
And a few small drops of rain;
I never had but one true-love,
In a cold grave she was lain.

'I'll do as much for my true-love
As any young man may;
I'll sit and mourn all at her grave
For a twelvemonth and a day.'

The twelvemonth and a day being up,
The dead began to speak:
'Oh who sits weeping on my grave,
And will not let me sleep?'

''Tis I, my love, sits on your grave,
And will not let you sleep;
For I crave one kiss of your clay-cold lips,
And that is all I seek.'

'You crave one kiss of my clay-cold lips;
But my breath smells earthy strong;
If you have one kiss of my clay-cold lips,
Your time will not be long.

''Tis down in yonder garden green,
Love, where we used to walk,
The finest flower that ere was seen
Is withered to a stalk.

'The stalk is withered dry my love,
So will our hearts decay;
So make yourself content, my love,
Till God calls you away.'

ANON.

The Ballad of Springhill

Music: PEGGY SEEGER
Words: PEGGY SEEGER and EWAN MACCOLL

In the town of Springhill; you don't sleep easy,
Often the earth will tremble and roll,
When the earth is restless, miners die,
Bone and blood is the price of coal,
Bone and blood is the price of coal.

In the town of Springhill, Nova Scotia,
Late in the year of fifty-eight,
Day still comes and the sun still shines,
But it's dark as the grave in the Cumberland Mine,
Dark as the grave in the Cumberland Mine.

Down at the coal face, miners working,
Rattle of the belt and the cutter's blade,
Rumble of rock and the walls close round
The living and the dead men two miles down,
Living and the dead men two miles down.

Twelve men lay two miles from the pitshaft,
Twelve men lay in the dark and sang,
Long, hot days in the miner's tomb,
It was three feet high and a hundred long,
  Three feet high and a hundred long.

Three days passed and the lamps gave out
And Caleb Rushton he up and said:
'There's no more water nor light nor bread
So we'll live on songs and hope instead.
  Live on songs and hope instead.'

Listen for the shouts of the *bareface miners*,
Listen through the rubble for a rescue team,
Six-hundred feet of coal and slag,
Hope imprisoned in a three-foot seam,
Hope imprisoned in a three-foot seam.

Eight days passed and some were rescued,
Leaving the dead to lie alone,
Through all their lives they dug a grave,
Two miles of earth for a marking stone,
Two miles of earth for a marking stone.

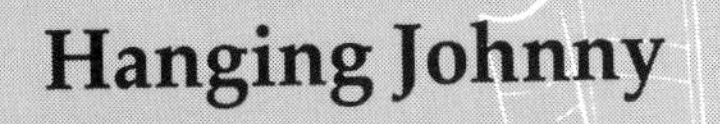

Hanging Johnny

They call me Hanging Johnny—
Away, boys, away!
They say I hanged a many—
Then hang, boys, hang!

They say I hanged my brother—
Away, boys, away!
They say I hanged my mother—
Then hang, boys, hang!

They say I hanged my Annie—
Away, boys, away!
I hanged her up so canny—
Then hang, boys, hang!

They say I hanged my daddy—
Away, boys, away!
But I never hanged no body—
Then hang, boys, hang!

ANON.

The Cherry-Tree Carol

Joseph was an old man,
  An old man was he
When he wedded Mary
  In the land of Galilee.

Joseph and Mary walking
  In the midst of a wood
Saw berries and cherries
  As red as the blood.

O then bespoke Mary,
  So meek and so mild,
'Pray get me one cherry,
  For I am with child.'

O then bespoke Joseph,
  So rude and unkind,
'Let him get thee a cherry
  That got thee with child.'

O then bespoke the babe
  Within his mother's womb,
'Bow down, thou tall cherry-tree,
  And give my mother some.'

Then bowed down the tall cherry-tree
  To his mother's right hand,
And she cried, 'See, Joseph,
  I have cherries at command!'

And Mary ate her cherry
  As red as the blood;
Then Mary went on
  With her heavy load.

ANON.

Mother and Maiden

I sing of a maiden
  That is matchless.
King of all kings
  For her son she chose.

He came all so still
  Where his mother was,
As dew in April
  That falleth on the grass.

He came all so still
  To his mother's bower,
As dew in April
  That falleth on the flower.

He came all so still—
  There his mother lay,
As dew in April
  That falleth on the spray.

Mother and maiden
  Was never none but she;
Well may such a lady
  God's mother be.

ANON.

Sea Shanty

Blow* the man down, bullies, blow the man down, *knock*
Way, ay—blow the man down!
O, blow the man down in Liverpool Town,
Give me some time to blow the man down!

'Twas on a Black Baller I first served my time,
And on that Black Baller I wasted my prime.

'Tis when a Black Baller is clear of the land,
Our boatswain first gives us the word of command.

'Lay aft,' is the cry, 'to the break of the poop,
Or I'll help you along with the toe of my boot!'

Then larboard and starboard on the deck you will sprawl,
For 'Kicking Jack Williams' commands that Black Ball.

'Tis when a Black Baller returns to her dock,
The lassies and lads to the pierhead do flock.

Blow the man down, bullies, blow the man down!
O, blow the man down in Liverpool Town.

As I was walking down Paradise Street,
A brass-bound policeman I happened to meet.

Says he: 'You're a Black-baller by the cut of your hair.
I know you're a Black-baller by the clothes that you wear.'

'O policeman, O policeman, you do me great wrong,
I'm a *Flying Fish* sailor, just home from Hong Kong.'

They gave me three months in Liverpool Town:
For booting and kicking and blowing him down.

ANON.

The Dying Cowboy

As I walked out in the streets of Laredo,
As I walked out in Laredo one day,
I spied a poor cowboy wrapped up in white linen,
Wrapped up in white linen as cold as the clay.

'I see by your outfit that you are a cowboy,'
These words he did say as I boldly stepped by.
'Come, sit down beside me and hear my sad story;
I was shot in the breast and I know I must die.

Once in my saddle I used to look handsome,
Once in my saddle I used to look gay.
I first went to drinkin' and then to card playin',
Got shot in the breast, which ended my day.

Let sixteen gamblers come handle my coffin,
Let sixteen girls come carry my pall;
Put bunches of roses all over my coffin,
Put roses to deaden the clods as they fall.

And beat the drums slowly and play the fife lowly,
And play the dead march as you carry me along;
Take me to the prairie and lay the sod o'er me,
For I'm a young cowboy and I know I've done wrong.'

We beat the drums slowly and played the fife lowly,
And bitterly wept as we bore him along;
For we all loved our comrade so brave, young and
handsome,
We loved the young cowboy although he'd done wrong. ANON.

John Polruddon*

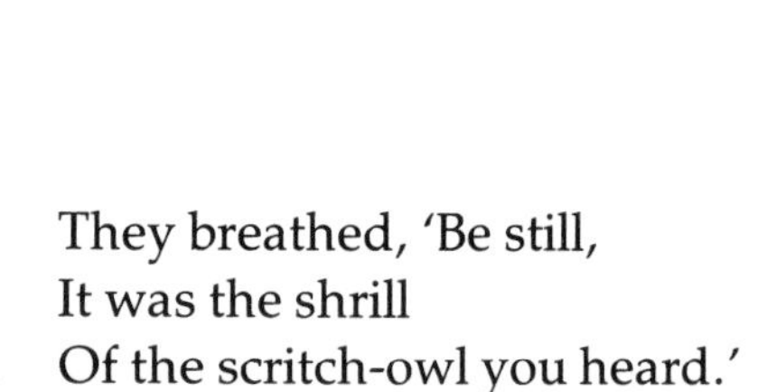

John Polruddon
All of a sudden
Went out of his house one night,

When a privateer
Came sailing near
Under his window-light.

They saw his jugs
His plates and mugs
His hearth as bright as brass,

His gews and gaws
And kicks and shaws
All through their spying-glass.

They saw his wine
His silver shine
They heard his fiddlers play.

'Tonight,' they said,
'Out of his bed
Polruddon we'll take away.'

And from a skiff
They climbed the cliff
And crossed the salt-wet lawn,

And as they crept
Polruddon slept
The night away to dawn.

'In air or ground
What is that sound?'
Polruddon said, and stirred.

They breathed, 'Be still,
It was the shrill
Of the scritch-owl you heard.'

'O yet again
I hear it plain,
But do I wake or dream?

'In morning's fog
The otter-dog
Is whistling by the stream.

'Now from the sea
What comes for me
Beneath my window dark?'

'Lie still, my dear,
All that you hear
Is the red fox's bark.'

Swift from his bed
Polruddon was sped
Before the day was white,

And head and feet
Wrapped in a sheet
They bore him down the height.

And never more
Through his own door
Polruddon went nor came,

Though many a tide
Has turned beside
The cliff that bears his name.

On stone and brick
Was ivy thick,
And the grey roof was thin,

And winter's gale
With fists of hail
Broke all the windows in.

The chimney-crown
It tumbled down
And up grew the green,

Till on the cliff
It was as if
A house had never been.

But when the moon
Swims late or soon
Across St Austell Bay,

What sight, what sound
Haunts air and ground
Where once Polruddon lay?

It is the high
White scritch-owl's cry,
The fox as dark as blood,

And on the hill
The otter still
Whistles beside the flood.

CHARLES CAUSLEY

*John Polruddon's house was on the cliff over Pentewan, in south Cornwall. The story of his disappearance dates from early Tudor times.

From Reynard the Fox

The pure clean air came sweet to his lungs,
Till he thought foul scorn on those crying tongues.
In a three mile more he would reach the haven
In the Wan Dyke croaked on by the raven.
In a three mile more he would make his berth
On the hard cool floor of a Wan Dyke earth,
Too deep for spade, too curved for terrier,
With the pride of the race to make rest the merrier.
In a three mile more he would reach his dream,
So his game heart gulped and he put on steam.

Like a rocket shot to a ship ashore
The lean red bolt of his body tore,
Like a ripple of wind running swift on grass,
Like a shadow on wheat when a cloud blows past,
Like a turn at the buoy in a cutter sailing
When the bright green gleam lips white at the railing,
Like the April snake whipping back to sheath,
Like the gannet's hurtle on fish beneath,
Like a kestrel chasing, like a sickle reaping,
Like all things swooping, like all things sweeping,
Like a hound for stay, like a stag for swift,
With his shadow beside like spinning drift.

Past the gibbet-stock all stuck with nails,
Where they hanged in chains what had hung at jails,
Past Ashmundshowe where Ashmund sleeps,
And none but the tumbling peewit weeps,
Past Curlew Calling, the gaunt grey corner
Where the curlew comes as a summer mourner,
Past Blowbury Beacon, shaking his fleece,
Where all winds hurry and none brings peace;
Then down on the mile-long green decline,
Where the turf's like spring and the air's like wine,
Where the sweeping spurs of the downland spill
Into Wan Brook Valley and Wan Dyke Hill.

On he went with a galloping rally
Past Maesbury Clump for Wan Brook Valley.
The blood in his veins went romping high,
'Get on, on, on, to the earth or die.'
The air of the downs went purely past
Till he felt the glory of going fast,
Till the terror of death, though there indeed,
Was lulled for a while by his pride of speed.
He was romping away from hounds and hunt,
He had Wan Dyke Hill and his earth in front,
In a one mile more when his point was made
He would rest in safety from dog or spade;
Nose between paws he would hear the shout
Of the 'Gone to earth!' to the hounds without,
The whine of the hounds, and their cat-feet gadding
Scratching the earth and their breath pad-padding;
He would hear the horn call hounds away,
And rest in peace till another day.

In one mile more he would lie at rest,
So for one mile more he would go his best.
He reached the dip at the long droop's end,
And he took what speed he had still to spend.
So down past Maesbury beech-clump grey
That would not be green till the end of May,
Past Arthur's Table, the white chalk boulder,
Where pasque flowers purple the down's grey shoulder,
Past Quichelm's Keeping, past Harry's Thorn,
To Thirty Acre all thin with corn.
As he raced the corn towards Wan Dyke Brook
The pack had view of the way he took;
Robin hallooed from the downland's crest,
He capped them on till they did their best.
The quarter-mile to the Wan Brook's brink
Was raced as quick as a man can think.

And here, as he ran to the huntsman's yelling,
The fox first felt that the pace was telling;
His body and lungs seemed all grown old,

His legs less certain, his heart less bold,
The hound-noise nearer, the hill-slope steeper,
The thud in the blood of his body deeper.
His pride in his speed, his joy in the race,
Were withered away, for what use was pace?
He had run his best, and the hounds ran better,
Then the going worsened, the earth was wetter.
Then his brush drooped down till it sometimes dragged,
And his fur felt sick and his chest was tagged
With taggles of mud, and his pads seemed lead,
It was well for him he'd an earth ahead.

Down he went to the brook and over,
Out of the corn and into the clover,
Over the slope that the Wan Brook drains,
Past Battle Tump where they earthed the Danes,
Then up the hill that the Wan Dyke rings
Where the Sarsen Stones stand grand like kings.
Seven Sarsens of granite grim,
As he ran them by they looked at him;
As he leaped the lip of their earthen paling
The hounds were gaining and he was failing.

He passed the Sarsens, he left the spur,
He pressed uphill to the blasted fir,
He slipped as he leaped the hedge; he slithered.
'He's mine,' thought Robin. 'He's done: he's dithered.'
At the second attempt he cleared the fence,
He turned half-right where the gorse was dense,
He was leading the hounds by a furlong clear.
He was past his best, but his earth was near.
He ran up gorse to the spring of the ramp,
The steep green wall of the dead men's camp,
He sidled up it and scampered down
To the deep green ditch of the Dead Men's Town.

Within, as he reached that soft green turf,
The wind, blowing lonely, moaned like surf,
Desolate ramparts rose up steep
On either side, for the ghosts to keep.
He raced the trench, past the rabbit warren,
Close-grown with moss which the wind made barren;
He passed the spring where the rushes spread,
And there in the stones was his earth ahead.
One last short burst upon failing feet—
There life lay waiting, so sweet, so sweet,
Rest in a darkness, balm for aches.

The earth was stopped. It was barred with stakes.

JOHN MASEFIELD

The History of the Flood

Bang Bang Bang
Said the nails in the Ark.

It's getting rather dark
Said the nails in the Ark.

For the rain is coming down
Said the nails in the Ark.

And you're all like to drown
Said the nails in the Ark.

Dark and black as sin
Said the nails in the Ark.

So won't you all come in
Said the nails in the Ark.

But only two by two
Said the nails in the Ark.

So they came in two by two,
The elephant, the kangaroo,
And the gnu,
And the little tiny shrew.

Then the birds
Flocked in like winged words:
Two racket-tailed motmots, two macaws,
Two nuthatches and two
Little bright robins.

And the reptiles: the gila monster, the slow-worm,
The green mamba, the cottonmouth and the alligator—
All squirmed in;
And after a very lengthy walk,
Two giant Galapagos tortoises.

And the insects in their hierarchies:
A queen ant, a king ant, a queen wasp, a king wasp,
A queen bee, a king bee,
And all the beetles, bugs and mosquitoes,
Cascaded in like glittering, murmurous jewels.

But the fish had their wish;
For the rain came down.
People began to drown:
The wicked, the rich—
They gasped out bubbles of pure gold,
Which exhalations
Rose to the constellations.

So for forty days and forty nights
They were on the waste of waters
In those cramped quarters.
It was very dark, damp and lonely.
There was nothing to see, but only
The rain which continued to drop.
It did not stop.

So Noah sent forth a Raven. The raven said 'Kark!
I will not go back to the Ark.'
The raven was footloose,
He fed on the bodies of the rich—
Rich with vitamins and goo.
They had become bloated,
And everywhere they floated.

The raven's heart was black,
He did not come back.

It was not a nice thing to do:
Which is why the raven is a token of wrath,
And creaks like a rusty gate
When he crosses your path; and Fate
Will grant you no luck that day:
The raven is fey:
You were meant to have a scare.
Fortunately in England
The raven is rather rare.

Then Noah sent forth a dove
She did not want to rove.
She longed for her love—
The other turtle dove—
(For her no other dove!)
She brought back a twig from an olive-tree.
There is no more beautiful tree
Anywhere on the earth,
Even when it comes to birth
From six weeks under the sea.

She did not want to rove.
She wanted to take her rest,
And to build herself a nest
All in the olive grove.
She wanted to make love.
She thought that was the best.

The dove was not a rover;
So they knew that the rain was over.
Noah and his wife got out
(They had become rather stout)
And Japhet, Ham and Shem.
(The same could be said of them.)
They looked up at the sky.
The earth was becoming dry.

Then the animals came ashore—
There were more of them than before:
There were two dogs and a litter of puppies;
There were a tom-cat and two tib-cats
And two litters of kittens—cats
Do not obey regulations;
And, as you might expect,
A quantity of rabbits.

God put a rainbow in the sky.
They wondered what it was for.
There had never been a rainbow before.
The rainbow was a sign;
It looked like a neon sign—
Seven colours arched in the skies:
What should it publicize?
They looked up with wondering eyes.

It advertises Mercy
Said the nails in the Ark.

Mercy Mercy Mercy
Said the nails in the Ark.

Our God is merciful
Said the nails in the Ark.

Merciful and gracious
Bang Bang Bang Bang.

JOHN HEATH-STUBBS

John Barleycorn

There were three kings into the east,
  Three kings both great and high;
And they hae sworn a solemn oath
  John Barleycorn should die.

They took a plough and plough'd him down,
  Put clods upon his head;
And they hae sworn a solemn oath
  John Barleycorn was dead.

But the cheerful Spring came kindly on,
  And show'rs began to fall;
John Barleycorn got up again,
  And sore surpris'd them all.

The sultry suns of Summer came,
  And he grew thick and strong;
His head weel arm'd wi' pointed spears,
  That no one should him wrong.

The sober Autumn enter'd mild,
  When he grew wan and pale;
His bending joints and drooping head
  Show'd he began to fail.

His colour sicken'd more and more,
  He faded into age;
And then his enemies began
  To show their deadly rage.

They've ta'en a weapon, long and sharp,
  And cut him by the knee;
Then tied him fast upon a cart,
  Like a rogue for forgerie.

They laid him down upon his back,
  And cudgell'd him full sore;

They hung him up before the storm,
And turn'd him o'er and o'er.

They filléd up a darksome pit
With water to the brim;
They heavéd in John Barleycorn,
There let him sink or swim.

They laid him out upon the floor,
To work him further woe:
And still, as signs of life appear'd,
They toss'd him to and fro.

They wasted o'er a scorching flame
The marrow of his bones;
But a miller us'd him worst of all—
He crush'd him 'tween two stones.

And they hae ta'en his very heart's blood,
And drank it round and round;
And still the more and more they drank,
Their joy did more abound.

John Barleycorn was a hero bold,
Of noble enterprise;
For if you do but taste his blood,
'Twill make your courage rise.

'Twill make a man forget his woe;
'Twill heighten all his joy;
'Twill make the widow's heart to sing,
Tho' the tear were in her eye.

Then let us toast John Barleycorn,
Each man a glass in hand;
And may his great posterity
Ne'er fail in old Scotland.

ROBERT BURNS

GO-KART

Me and my mate Harrybo
we once made a go-kart.
Everyone was making go-karts
so we had to make one.
Big Tony's was terrific,
Big Tony was terrific
because Big Tony told us he was.
What he said was,
'I am TERRIFIC,'
And because Big Tony was VERY big
no one said,
'Big Tony.
You are NOT terrific.'
So,
Big Tony was terrific
and Big Tony's go-kart was terrific.
And that was that.

When Big Tony sat on his go-kart
he looked like a real driver.
He had control.
When he came down a road round our way
called Moss Lane
he could make the wind blow his hair,
pheeeeeeoooooooooph,
he could make the wheels of his go-kart go
prrrrrrrrrrrrrrr
and he went
eeeeeeeeeeeeooowwwwwww
as he went past.
I was jealous of Big Tony.
I was afraid that I thought
he might be
terrific.

So me and Harrybo
we made a go-kart
out of his old pram
and some boxes and crates
we got from the off-licence.
We nailed it up with bent nails
but Harrybo's dad said,
'No no no no no
you should use big metal staples,'
And he gave us some.
He said they were
Heavy Duty.

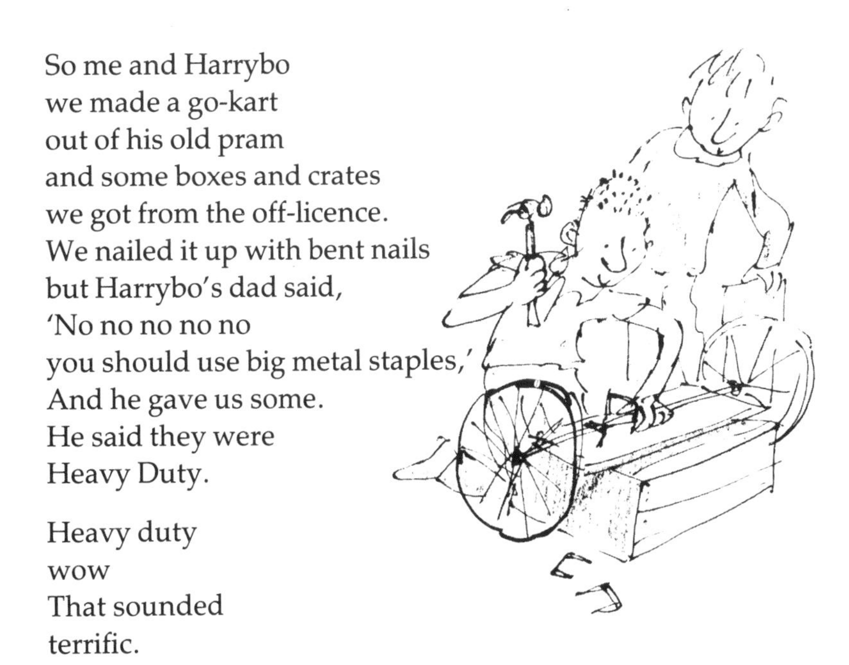

Heavy duty
wow
That sounded
terrific.

So then we tied cord round the front cross-piece.
But Harrybo's dad said,
'No no no no no,
you should use the pram handle.'
And he helped us fix
the pram handle to the cross-piece
He said, 'That'll give you
Control.'

Control
wow
That sounded
terrific.

Harrybo sat on the beer-crate
and steered,
I kneeled behind.
But Harrybo's dad said,

'No no no no no
you should kneel on foam pads.'
And he cut these two foam pads
for me to kneel on.
Harrybo's dad said,
'That'll help you
Last The Course.'

Last the course,
wow
That sounded
terrific.

Our go-kart was ready.

So we took it up to the top of Moss Lane
and Harrybo said,
'I'll steer,' and he did.
It was fan
tastic.
It felt just like Big Tony looked.
The hair in the wind
pheeeeeeeooooooooooph
the wheels
prrrrrrrrrrrrrrr
and so we both went
eeeeeeeeeeeeeoooowwwwwwwww

So we took it up to the top
of Moss Lane again
and Harrybo said,
'I'll steer,'
and he did.

It was a-
mazing.
The road went blurry.

The hair in the wind
pheeeeeeeoooooph
the wheels went
prrrrrrrrrrrr
so we both went
eeeeeeeeeoooowwwwwwwww

So we took it up to the top of Moss Lane again
and Harrybo said,
'I'll steer,'
so I said,
'Can I have a go?'

Harrybo said,
'NO.'
'Go on,' I said.
'No,' he said, 'You've never done it.'
'Go on, Harrybo. Let me have a go.
Go on. I mean. Blimey.
Come on, Harrybo. Go on.'
'No.'
'Oh go on. Go on. Go on.'

'All right,' he said.
'Look out, won't you.'
'Yeah yeah yeah. *I* know,' I said.
I thought,
'I'm going to be
terrific.'
My hair—pheeeoooph
wheels—prrrrrr
me—eeeow

And away we went
Hair—yeah—pheeeeeeeeoooph
wheels—yeah—prrrrrrrrrrr
me—yeah—eeeeeeeeoooooow
BUT
halfway down Moss Lane

there's Moss Close
and that's where the road curves
and that's where Big Tony steers
Big Tony leans
Big Tony controls
prrrrrrrrrr
eeeeeeeoooowwww
I saw Moss Close coming up really fast . . .
'Steer.' shouts Harrybo. 'Steer, you big wally!'
And I yanked on the pram handle
uh
and the whole world
went round once and twice
and three times
and my head went rolling
down the road
pulling me after it
and the go-kart came for the ride
over and over and over
until my nose and my chin
and my two front teeth landed up
in the grit of the gutter.
Harrybo was crying.
'Wo wo wo oooo wo wo ooo.'
I breathed in and it whistled.
'Whew.'
'Whew.'
There it was again.
I stuck my finger up to my tooth
and it was chipped.
Harrybo said,
'Your chin's bleeding,'
and I said,
'Your chin's bleeding an' all.'
'I know ooooooo,' he said.

We walked home.
He pulled the kart,
got to his place

he didn't say anything.
Nothing at all.
Not a word.
And he went in.
I walked on to my place
'Whew—whew—whew,'
it was still whistling.

When I got in
I told Mum everything
and she said, well, she said all kinds of things—
like, 'Well—your teeth'll
probably fall out, you know.'
One of those nice things
that mums say.

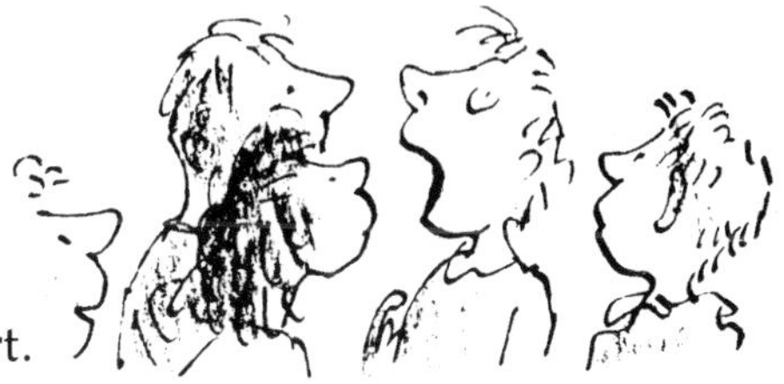

Next day at school
they were all asking about the crash
they all looked at my tooth
and they all wanted to see the go-kart.
Harrybo said,
'You can't,
cos my dad's
chopped it up.'

Chopped up.
Wow
that sounded
terrible.

Hey,
when Harrybo got his racer,
his brand new racing bike for Christmas
I didn't ask him for a go on it.
I didn't
no
I didn't.

I wonder why.

MICHAEL ROSEN

Ballads and stories need to be shared and performed. We have already suggested ways in which you could write your own ballads (p. 28) and, of course, some of the poems in this section invite illustrations; but the most important thing is to hear them aloud. Practise your reading and, if you have only a few lines to say, try to learn them.

★ *Go-Kart* (p. 68) can be read aloud using three voices and three noises! You will need someone for the narrator who speaks most of the lines and two other readers for Harrybo and his dad. The noises of the wind, the wheels and the 'racing go-kart' could be done by one person in charge of sound effects or by three separate voices. Rehearse the poem in groups. You will probably have several quite different performances in the class.

★ *The Cherry-Tree Carol* (p. 52) and *Mother and Maiden* (p. 53) can both be read aloud by four voices. In the first, you will need a narrator, Joseph, Mary and Jesus; also, you may be able to work out some simple movements to help you dramatise the reading. *Mother and Maiden* is a more delicate poem; handle it with care! Perhaps one person could speak the first and last verses and three other voices could each take one of the middle verses.

★ *Hanging Johnny* (p. 51) needs a single voice for Johnny while the rest of the class speak the sailors' lines (in italics) all together. Imagine you are hauling on the ropes and try to get the rhythm of the work into the way you say the lines. Again, some simple movements will help. With a little practice you should be able to manage without the book.

★ *The History of the Flood* (p. 62) lends itself to a tape-recorded reading and to illustration. The nails in the Ark are heard at the beginning and end of the poem; you might have sound effects behind the first seven sections and the last four sections of the poem. The actual reading of the sections can be shared out in various ways but you might experiment with choral speaking for the nails and, in between, different individual voices for the sections on the birds, the reptiles, the insects, the fish, the raven (2), the dove (3), the coming ashore and the rainbow. A frieze of pictures—perhaps pairs could work on particular creatures—could accompany your reading.

Creatures

Bat

At evening, sitting on this terrace,
When the sun from the west, beyond Pisa, beyond the
mountains of Carrara
Departs, and the world is taken by surprise . . .

When the tired flower of Florence is in gloom beneath the
glowing
Brown hills surrounding . . .
When under the arches of the Ponte Vecchio
A green light enters against stream, flush from the west,
Against the current of obscure Arno . . .

Look up, and you see things flying
Between the day and the night;
Swallows with spools of dark thread sewing the shadows
together.

A circle swoop, and a quick parabola under the bridge arches
Where light pushes through;
A sudden turning upon itself of a thing in the air.
A dip to the water.

And you think:
'The swallows are flying so late!'

Swallows?

Dark air-life looping
Yet missing the pure loop . . .
A twitch, a twitter, an elastic shudder in flight
And serrated wings against the sky,
Like a glove, a black glove thrown up at the light,
And falling back.

Never swallows!
Bats!
The swallows are gone.

At a wavering instant the swallows give way to bats
By the Ponte Vecchio . . .
Changing guard.

Bats, and an uneasy creeping in one's scalp
As the bats swoop overhead!
Flying madly.

Pipistrello!
Black piper on an infinitesimal pipe.
Little lumps that fly in air and have voices indefinite, wildly
vindictive;

Wings like bits of umbrella.

Bats!

Creatures that hang themselves up like an old rag, to sleep;
And disgustingly upside down.
Hanging upside down like rows of disgusting old rags
And grinning in their sleep.
Bats!

In China the bat is symbol of happiness.

Not for me!

D. H. LAWRENCE

The Swallows

All day—when early morning shone
With every dewdrop its own dawn
And when cockchafers were abroad
Hurtling like missiles that had lost their road—

The swallows twisting here and there
Round unseen corners in the air
Upstream and down so quickly passed
I wondered that their shadows flew as fast.

They steeple-chased over the bridge
And dropped down to a drowning midge
Sharing the river with the fish,
Although the air itself was their chief dish.

Blue-winged snowballs! until they turned
And then with ruddy breasts they burned;
All in one instant everywhere,
Jugglers with their own bodies in the air

ANDREW YOUNG

The Eagle

He clasps the crag with hookéd hands;
Close to the sun in lonely lands,
Ringed with the azure world, he stands.

The wrinkled sea beneath him crawls;
He watches from his mountain walls,
And like a thunderbolt he falls.

LORD TENNYSON

The Eagle

He hangs between his wings outspread
  Level and still
And bends a narrow golden head,
  Scanning the ground to kill.

Yet as he sails and smoothly swings
  Round the hill-side,
He looks as though from his own wings
  He hung down crucified.

ANDREW YOUNG

The Bird-Fancier

Up to his shoulders
In grasses coarse as silk,
The white cat with the yellow eyes
Sits with all four paws together,
Tall as a quart of milk.

He hardly moves his head
To touch with nice nose
What his wary whiskers tell him
Is here a weed
And here a rose.

On a dry stick he rubs his jaws,
And the thin
Corners of his smile
Silently mew when a leaf
Tickles his chin.

With a neat grimace
He nips a new
Blade of feathery grass,
Flicks from his ear
A grain of dew.

His sleepy eyes are wild with birds.
Every sparrow, thrush and wren
Widens their furred horizons
Till their flying song
Narrows them again.

JAMES KIRKUP

Milk for the Cat

When the tea is brought at five o'clock,
And all the neat curtains are drawn with care,
The little black cat with bright green eyes
Is suddenly purring there.

At first she pretends, having nothing to do,
She has come in merely to blink by the grate,
But, though tea may be late or the milk may be sour,
She is never late.

And presently her agate eyes
Take a soft large milky haze,
And her independent casual glance
Becomes a stiff hard gaze.

Then she stamps her claws or lifts her ears
Or twists her tail and begins to stir,
Till suddenly all her lithe body becomes
One breathing trembling purr.

The children eat and wriggle and laugh;
The two old ladies stroke their silk:
But the cat is grown small and thin with desire,
Transformed to a creeping lust for milk.

The white saucer like some full moon descends
At last from the clouds of the table above;
She sighs and dreams and thrills and glows,
Transfigured with love.

She nestles over the shining rim,
Buries her chin in the creamy sea;
Her tail hangs loose; each drowsy paw
Is doubled under each bending knee.

A long dim ecstasy holds her life;
 Her world is an infinite shapeless white,
Till her tongue has curled the last holy drop,
 Then she sinks back into the night.

Draws and dips her body to heap
 Her sleepy nerves in the great arm-chair,
Lies defeated and buried deep
 Three or four hours unconscious there.

HAROLD MONRO

The Cat and the Moon

The cat went here and there
And the moon spun round like a top,
And the nearest kin of the moon,
The creeping cat, looked up.
Black Minnaloushe stared at the moon,
For, wander and wail as he would,
The pure cold light in the sky
Troubled his animal blood.
Minnaloushe runs in the grass
Lifting his delicate feet.
Do you dance, Minnaloushe, do you dance?
When two close kindred meet,
What better than call a dance?
Maybe the moon may learn,
Tired of that courtly fashion,
A new dance turn.
Minnaloushe creeps through the grass
From moonlit place to place,
The sacred moon overhead
Has taken a new phase.
Does Minnaloushe know that his pupils
Will pass from change to change,
And that from round to crescent,
From crescent to round they range?
Minnaloushe creeps through the grass
Alone, important and wise,
And lifts to the changing moon
His changing eyes.

W. B. YEATS

The Moth

Isled in the midnight air,
Musked with the dark's faint bloom,
Out into glooming and secret haunts
  The flame cries, 'Come!'

Lovely in dye and fan,
A-tremble in shimmering grace,
A moth from her winter swoon
  Uplifts her face:

Stares from her glamorous eyes;
Wafts her on plumes like mist;
In ecstasy swirls and sways
  To her strange tryst.

WALTER DE LA MARE

The Bells of Heaven

'Twould ring the bells of Heaven
The wildest peal for years,
If Parson lost his senses
And people came to theirs,
And he and they together
Knelt down with angry prayers
For tamed and shabby tigers
And dancing dogs and bears,
And wretched, blind pit ponies,
And little hunted hares.

RALPH HODGSON

The Tigress

They trapped her in the Indian hills
And put her in a box; and though so young
The dockers quailed to hear her voice
As she made war on every bolt and thong.

Now she paces, sleeps on her ledge,
Glares, growls, excretes, gnaws lumps of meat,
Sun and shadow in iron bars
Dropping about her and a listless mate.

CLIFFORD DYMENT

A Dead Mole

Strong-shouldered mole,
That so much lived below the ground,
Dug, fought and loved, hunted and fed,
For you to raise a mound
Was as for us to make a hole;
What wonder now that being dead
Your body lies here stout and square
Buried within the blue vault of the air?

ANDREW YOUNG

The Sloth

In moving-slow he has no Peer.
You ask him something in his ear,
He thinks about it for a year;

And, then, before he says a Word
There, upside down (unlike a Bird),
He will assume that you have Heard—

A most Ex-as-per-at-ing Lug.
But should you call his manner Smug,
He'll sigh and give his Branch a Hug;

Then off again to Sleep he goes,
Still swaying gently by his Toes,
And you just *know* he knows he knows.

THEODORE ROETHKE

Diary of a Church Mouse

Here among long-discarded cassocks,
Damp stools, and half-split open hassocks,
Here where the Vicar never looks
I nibble through old service books.
Lean and alone I spend my days
Behind this Church of England baize.
I share my dark forgotten room
With two oil-lamps and half a broom.
The cleaner never bothers me,
So here I eat my frugal tea.
My bread is sawdust mixed with straw;
My jam is polish for the floor.
   Christmas and Easter may be feasts
For congregations and for priests,
And so may Whitsun. All the same,
They do not fill my meagre frame.
For me the only feast at all
Is Autumn's Harvest Festival,
When I can satisfy my want
With ears of corn around the font.
I climb the eagle's brazen head
To burrow through a loaf of bread.
I scramble up the pulpit stair
And gnaw the marrows hanging there.
   It is enjoyable to taste
These items ere they go to waste,
But how annoying when one finds
That other mice with pagan minds
Come into church my food to share
Who have no proper business there.
Two field mice who have no desire

To be baptized, invade the choir.
A large and most unfriendly rat
Comes in to see what we are at.
He says he thinks there is no God
And yet he comes . . . it's rather odd.
This year he stole a sheaf of wheat
(It screened our special preacher's seat).
And prosperous mice from fields away
Came in to hear the organ play,
And under cover of its notes
Ate through the altar's sheaf of oats.
A Low Church mouse, who thinks that I
Am too papistical, and High,
Yet somehow doesn't think it wrong
To munch through Harvest Evensong,
While I, who starve the whole year through,
Must share my food with rodents who
Except at this time of the year
Not once inside the church appear.
Within the human world I know
Such goings-on could not be so,
For human beings only do
What their religion tells them to.
They read the Bible every day
And always, night and morning, pray,
And just like me, the good church mouse,
Worship each week in God's own house.
But all the same it's strange to me
How very full the church can be
With people I don't see at all
Except at Harvest Festival.

JOHN BETJEMAN

Ducks

I
From troubles of the world
I turn to ducks,
Beautiful comical things
Sleeping or curled
Their heads beneath white wings
By water cool,
Or finding curious things
To eat in various mucks
Beneath the pool,
Tails uppermost, or waddling
Sailor-like on the shores
Of ponds, or paddling
—Left! right!—with fanlike feet
Which are for steady oars
When they (white galleys) float
Each bird a boat
Rippling at will the sweet
Wide waterway . . .
When night is fallen *you* creep
Upstairs, but drakes and dillies
Nest with pale water-stars,
Moonbeams and shadow bars
And water-lilies:
Fearful too much to sleep

Since they've no locks
To click against the teeth
Of weasel and fox.
And warm beneath
Are eggs of cloudy green
When hungry rats and lean
Would stealthily suck
New life, but for the mien,
The bold ferocious mien
Of the mother-duck.

II
Yes, ducks are valiant things
On nests of twigs and straws,
And ducks are soothy things
And lovely on the lake
When that the sunlight draws
Thereon their pictures dim
In colours cool.
And when beneath the pool
They dabble, and when they swim
And make their rippling rings,
O ducks are beautiful things!

But ducks are comical things:
As comical as you.
Quack!
They waddle round, they do.
They eat all sorts of things.

And then they quack.
By barn and stable and stack
They wander at their will,
But if you go too near
They look at you through black
Small topaz-tinted eyes.
And wish you ill.
Triangular and clear
They leave their curious track
In mud at the water's edge,
And there amid the sedge
And slime they gobble and peer
Saying 'Quack! quack!'

III
When God had finished the stars and whirl of coloured suns
He turned His mind from big things to fashion little ones,
Beautiful tiny things (like daisies) He made, and then
He made the comical ones in case the minds of men
  Should stiffen and become
  Dull, humourless and glum:
And so forgetful of their Maker be
As to take even themselves—*quite seriously*.
Caterpillars and cats are lively and excellent puns:
All God's jokes are good—even the practical ones!
And as for the duck, I think God must have smiled a bit
Seeing those eyes blink on the day He fashioned it.
And He's probably laughing still at the sound that came out
  of its bill!

F. W. HARVEY

Mooses

The goofy Moose, the walking house-frame,
Is lost
In the forest. He bumps, he blunders, he stands.

With massy bony thoughts sticking out near his ears—
Reaching out palm upwards, to catch whatever might be
falling from heaven—
He tries to think,
Leaning their huge weight
On the lectern of his front legs.

He can't find the world!
Where did it go? What does a world look like?
The Moose
Crashes on, and crashes into a lake, and stares at the
mountain, and cries
'Where do I belong? This is no place!'

He turns and drags half the lake out after him
And charges the cackling underbrush—

He meets another Moose.
He stares, he thinks 'It's only a mirror!'

'Where is the world?' he groans, 'O my lost world!
And why am I so ugly?
And why am I so far away from my feet?'

He weeps.
Hopeless drops drip from his droopy lips.

The other Moose just stands there doing the same.

Two dopes of the deep woods.

TED HUGHES

The Kangaroo

Traditional Australian

Old Jumpety-Bumpety-Hop-and-Go-One
Was lying asleep on his side in the sun.
This old Kangaroo, he was whisking the flies
(With his long glossy tail) from his ears and his eyes.
Jumpety-Bumpety-Hop-and-Go-One
Was lying asleep on his side in the sun,
Jumpety-Bumpety-Hop!

ANON.

★ **Portrait gallery.** Look at D. H. Lawrence's poem *Bat* on p. 75 and see how he arranges his ideas and phrases. Notice the things that Lawrence does and does not do. He does not bother with rhyme; he varies the length of the lines; and he uses comparisons. Discuss with your teacher the reasons why Lawrence chooses to do each of these things.

Now write your own poem in the same style. Jot down some notes. Here are some ideas which may help you to begin. Think of any creature: it may be a pet, a farm animal, or a wild one, and write down one or two words or phrases suggested by the following questions:

Where do you imagine your animal to be? Put it in its setting.
Is it moving or still?
What colour is it? Are there any markings on its body?
What would it be like to touch?
Now describe its face. Look especially at its eyes and mouth.
What is its expression? Does this suggest its feelings or thoughts?
What are your feelings about it? Do you think other people regard the animal in the same way?

Now that you have made your notes, remember the three things we noticed about Lawrence's *Bat*, and then write your own poem using your notes. When you have finished, illustrate your fair copy for display as part of a portrait gallery of animals.

★ **Poster poem.** Design an eagle poster. Both the poems on p. 78 give vivid pictures. How do you see the two eagles in your mind's eye? Perhaps the first one stands on a cliff-top with the sun behind him; the second one is hunting and his shape is compared with a crucifixion. Choose one and design a poster to include the poem and your illustration. Make your picture bold and colourful.

★ **Zoo visit.** Many people have mixed feelings about zoos. It's interesting to see so many unusual creatures from other countries but it may seem unfair to keep them in captivity. Talk in pairs about your visits to zoos, which creatures you particularly remember and what your feelings were when you saw the animals. Then, on your own, focus on *one* creature and jot down some notes about it from two points of view: first, as you remember it (a description of its colour, size, movements, noises, etc., just as you saw it in its cage); then, imagine you *are* the creature and write about what you see and feel as you gaze out at the world. Write up your poem in two contrasting sections.

★ **Display.** You'll need a collection of pictures—cut-outs from newspapers and magazines, post-cards, etc.—of animals, birds and insects. Perhaps each member of the class could provide two or three that they like. Talk in groups about the pictures you have brought:

– Are there any creatures you don't like?

– Are there any particular animal characters?

Then, on your own, choose *one* picture that appeals to you and write a short poem to go with it. When you've finished arrange your picture and poem on a single sheet as part of a class display.

City

The Excavation

Clusters of electric bulbs
Like giant chrysanthemums
Paint the black cavern
With streaks and blots
Of faded yellow.
In grotesque mimicry
The monstrous shadows
Ape each movement of toiling men.
The stale pungent odour of unpacked earth
Tickles the nostrils.
Through the wood-plank roof
The dull-booming rumble
Of scampering traffic
Trickles in—
But is swallowed up
By the harsh purr of the drill
As it bites frenziedly
Into the dogged rock.

Overhead, unseen,
A mountain of stone is kept upright
By a slender steel beam
And a theory.

MAX ENDICOFF

Out in the City

When you're out in the city
Shuffling down the street,
A bouncy city rhythm
Starts to boogie in your feet.

It jumps off the pavement,
There's a snare drum in your brain,
It pumps through your heart
Like a diesel train.

There's Harry on the corner,
Sings, 'How she goin' boy?'
To loose and easy Winston
With his brother Leroy.

Shout, 'Hello!' to Billy Brisket
With his tripes and cows heels,
Blood-stained rabbits
And trays of live eels.

Maltese Tony
Smoking in the shade
Keeping one good eye
On the amusement arcade.

And everybody's talking:

Move along
Step this way
Here's a bargain
What you say?
Mind your backs
Here's your stop
More fares?
Room on top.

Neon lights and take-aways
Gangs of boys and girls
Football crowds and market stalls
Taxi cabs and noise.

From the city cafes
On the smoky breeze
Smells of Indian cooking
Greek and Cantonese.

Well, some people like suburban life
Some people like the sea
Others like the countryside
But it's the city
Yes it's the city
It's the city life
For me.

GARETH OWEN

Song of the City

My brain is stiff with concrete
My limbs are rods of steel
My belly's stuffed with money
My soul was bought in a deal.

They poured metal through my arteries
They choked my lungs with lead
They churned my blood to plastic
They put murder into my head.

I'd a face like a map of the weather
Flesh that grew to the bone
But they tore my story out of my eyes
And turned my heart to stone.

Let me wind from my source like a river
Let me grow like wheat from the grain
Let me hold out my arms like a natural tree
Let my children love me again.

GARETH OWEN

The Seal

Throb, throb from the mixer
Spewing out concrete.
And at the heads of the cables
Stand the serpent-warders.
Sweating and straining,
Thrusting those cruel mouths to their prey.
Hark how the steel tongues hiss
As they stab.
The men sway under the effort,
And their eyes are bloodshot with the din,
The clatter that shatters the brain.
Throb, throb from the mixer
Spewing out concrete.

The crowd stands by
Watching the smoothers;
Fascinated by the flat, wet levels
Of newlaid cement,
See how those curdled lakes
Glisten under the sky,
Virginal.

Then the dusty air suddenly divides,
And a pigeon from a plane tree
Flutters down to bathe its wings in that mirage of water.

But deceived, and angry,
Bewildered by the din,
The throb, throb from the mixer
Spewing out concrete,
It backs upon its wing,
Threshes air, and is gone.

But there, in the deflowered bed,
Is the seal of its coral foot,
Set till rocks crumble.

RICHARD CHURCH

Tower-Block

Think of this tower-block
as if it was a street standing up
and instead of toing and froing
in buses and cars
you up and down it
in a high speed lift.

There will be no pavement artists of course
because there aren't any pavements.
There isn't room for a market
but then there isn't room for cars.
No cars: no accidents
but don't lean
out of the windows
don't play in the lifts
or they won't work.
They don't work
and they won't work
if you play Split Kipper,
Fox and Chickens, Dittyback,
Keek-bogle, Jackerback,
Huckey-buck, Hotchie-pig,
Foggy-plonks, Ching Chang Cholly
or Bunky-Bean Bam-Bye.

Go down. The stairs are outside—
you can't miss them—try not to miss them, please.
No pets.
Think how unhappy they'd be
locked in a tower-block.
There will be
no buskers, no hawkers
no flowers, no chinwaggers
no sandwich boards,
no passers-by,
except for
low-flying aircraft
or high-flying sparrows.

Here is a note from Head Office:
you will love your neighbour
left right above below
so no music, creaky boots,
caterwauling somersaulting—
never never never jump up or down
or you may
never never never get down or up again.
No questions.
It's best to tip-toe,
creep, crawl, and whisper.
If there *are* any
problems phone me
and I'll be out.
Good day.

MICHAEL ROSEN

Prelude

The winter evening settles down
With smell of steaks in passageways.
Six o'clock.
The burnt-out ends of smoky days.
And now a gusty shower wraps
The grimy scraps
Of withered leaves about your feet,
And newspapers from vacant lots;
The showers beat
On broken blinds and chimney-pots,
And at the corner of the street
A lonely cab-horse steams and stamps.
And then the lighting of the lamps.

T. S. ELIOT

★ **Poem and picture.** L. S. Lowry's picture (p. 101) of Salford as it used to be is drawn as though he were looking at the street from a top-storey window. Gareth Owen's *Song of the City* (p. 100) gives a different view of the city through modern eyes. Working in pairs, look at the picture first. What details do you notice about the street and the people? What impression do you get of the city in the background? Now, take it in turns to read the poem aloud to each other. Is it a sad or a happy song? What's happened to the city? What does it hope for in the last verse? Once you have talked about the picture and the poem with your partner, share your ideas with the rest of the class.

★ **Word-pictures**

- Imagine you are looking through one of those slits that builders leave in wooden boards surrounding a building site. The builders are working on the foundations. Look at the general scene, then pick out any details that attract your attention—a yellow mechanical digger . . . a bulldozer . . . a cement-mixer . . . cables . . . trenches. Describe, in a poem, what you see.
- *Prelude* (p. 105) describes a city landscape at 6 o'clock on a winter's evening. Choose a place, a season, and a time and make your own word-picture of somewhere you know.

★ **Performances**

- *Out in the City* (p. 96) is a poem for many voices. Share out the verses so that as many people as possible take part. You can fit a lot of voices in where 'everybody's talking' half-way through. When you have sorted out who says what, you may be able to add some simple movements to your performance. After all, it's a poem about 'shuffling down' a busy city street.
- *Tower-Block* (p. 103) is probably best read by two voices, the second one taking over with the 'note from Head Office' at the beginning of the last section. A pair of readers could rehearse it for performance. There are some tongue-twisters; and the pace and humour are both tricky.

Country

Geography Lesson

With Highland hair and arms of Wales
Reaching for Ireland, England trails
A lonely distance behind Europe
Trying impossibly to cheer up:
A sloppy nurse who hopes that maybe
No one will see she's dropped her baby
Splash into the Irish Sea
While bouncing it upon her knee.
With hips of Norfolk, bum of Kent,
Her posture's more than strangely bent.
Yorkshire gives backache with its Ridings.
The Midlands, full of railway sidings,
She blames for burps of indigestion.
Her Birmingham has got congestion.
Her Derbyshire is full of holes.
London's asleep at the controls
And her subconscious shifts the worry
Out to Middlesex and Surrey.
Yet Devon's a comfortable shoe
From which old Cornwall's toes peep through.
On Lleyn, sedately, Anglesey
Is balanced like a cup of tea,
While clucking in her tea-time mirth
Her mouth's the open Solway Firth
Ready to swallow if she can
The little cake of the Isle of Man.

Even asleep she falls apart:
Dreams of the Orkneys make her start
And stitches of the Isle of Wight
Drop off from Hampshire in the night.
With bits of knitting in the Channel,
Most of East Anglia wrapped in flannel
And snores exhaling from Argyll,
The dear old lady makes you smile:
What can you do with such a creature
To whom each county lends a feature?

She'll still be there when I am gone.
Through all *your* lives she'll shamble on,
Grubby, forgetful, laughing, hatless—
The silliest country in the atlas.

JOHN FULLER

The Lonely Scarecrow

My poor old bones—I've only two—
A broomshank and a broken stave.
My ragged gloves are a disgrace.
My one peg-foot is in the grave.

I wear the labourer's old clothes:
Coat, shirt and trousers all undone.
I bear my cross upon a hill
In rain and shine, in snow and sun.

I cannot help the way I look.
My funny hat is full of hay.
—O, wild birds, come and nest in me!
Why do you always fly away?

JAMES KIRKUP

Scarecrow

the scarecrow
looks sad tonight all covered in rags
her solitude made of sticks
flapping in the dark field
and her eyes that won't shut
watching the cows at sleep.
with no shoes
and wind in her pockets,
she counts those stars
she can see
from her fixed angle
and listens to the black sticks rubbing
as she spits her curses at the moon.

STEF PIXNER

Cornfield

(*by John Nash*)

These cornsheaves corded waist-high
prided with the dry bells of harvest,
bow earthwards offering back seed
to the cradling dark,
shadows thrown
silent as barefoot peasants
grown tall with evening,
moving slowly as the sun.

PHOEBE HESKETH

Weathers

This is the weather the cuckoo likes,
  And so do I;
When showers betumble the chestnut spikes,
  And nestlings fly:
And the little brown nightingale bills his best,
And they sit outside at 'The Travellers' Rest,'
And maids come forth sprig-muslin drest,
And citizens dream of the south and west,
  And so do I.

This is the weather the shepherd shuns,
  And so do I;
When beeches drip in browns and duns,
  And thresh, and ply;
And hill-hid tides throb, throe on throe,
And meadow rivulets overflow,
And drops on gate-bars hang in a row,
And rooks in families homeward go,
  And so do I.

THOMAS HARDY

Mid-Country Blow

All night and all day the wind roared in the trees,
Until I could think there were waves rolling high as my
  bedroom floor;
When I stood at the window, an elm bough swept to my
  knees;
The blue spruce lashed like a surf at the door.

The second dawn I would not have believed:
The oak stood with each leaf stiff as a bell.
When I looked at the altered scene, my eye was undeceived,
But my ear still kept the sound of the sea like a shell.

THEODORE ROETHKE

An Autumn Morning

The autumn morning, waked by many a gun,
Throws o'er the fields her many-coloured light,
Wood wildly touched, close tanned, and stubbles dun,
A motley paradise for earth's delight;
Clouds ripple as the darkness breaks to light,
And clover plots are hid with silver mist,
One shower of cobwebs o'er the surface spread;
And threads of silk in strange disorder twist
Round every leaf and blossom's bottly head;
Hares in the drowning herbage scarcely steal
But on the battered pathway squat abed
And by the cart-rut nip their morning meal.
Look where we may, the scene is strange and new,
And every object wears a changing hue.

JOHN CLARE

Clearing at Dawn

The fields are chill, the sparse rain has stopped;
The colours of Spring teem on every side.
With leaping fish the blue pond is full;
With singing thrushes the green boughs droop.
The flowers of the field have dabbled their powdered cheeks;
The mountain grasses are bent level at the waist.
By the bamboo stream the last fragment of cloud
Blown by the wind slowly scatters away.

From the Chinese, by LI PO
(*Trans. Arthur Waley*)

Tall Nettles

Tall nettles cover up, as they have done
These many springs, the rusty harrow, the plough
Long worn out, and the roller made of stone:
Only the elm butt tops the nettles now.

This corner of the farmyard I like most:
As well as any bloom upon a flower
I like the dust on the nettles, never lost
Except to prove the sweetness of a shower.

EDWARD THOMAS

Winter the Huntsman

Through his iron glades
Rides Winter the Huntsman,
All colour fades
As his horn is heard sighing.

Far through the forest
His wild hooves crash and thunder
Till many a mighty branch
Is torn asunder.

And the red reynard creeps
To his hole near the river,
The copper leaves fall
And the bare trees shiver.

As night creeps from the ground,
Hides each tree from its brother,
And each dying sound
Reveals yet another.

Is it Winter the Huntsman
Who gallops through his iron glades,
Cracking his cruel whip
To the gathering shades?

OSBERT SITWELL

Housing Scheme

All summer through
The field drank showers of larksong;
Offering in return
The hospitality of grasses,
And flowers kneedeep.

Over those wide acres
Trooped the plovers,
Mourning and lamenting as evening fell.
From the deep hedgerows
Where the foam of meadowsweet broke,
The rabbits and mice
Peeped out, and boldly sat in the sun.

But when the oaks were bronzing,
Steamrollers and brickcarts
Broke through the hedges.
The white-haired grasses, and the seedpods
Disappeared into the mud,
And the larks were silent, the plovers gone.

Then over the newlaid roads
And the open trenches of drains,
Rose a hoarding to face the highway,
'Build your house in the country.'

RICHARD CHURCH

★ **That looks like . . .** You may have played the game that John Fuller plays in *Geography Lesson* (p. 107). Can you add a pair of rhyming lines for any other part of the country?

Maps of other countries may suggest ideas and comparisons to you. Italy looks as if it's booting Sicily into the Mediterranean; in the poem on p. 196, Judith Wright sees what appears to be the shape of a hare crouching in the landscape of the full moon. Have a look through an atlas at the shape of the seas and the continents. When you have found an outline that suggests a comparison, trace or draw it, and write a few lines about the comparison you have noticed.

★ **Picture into poem.** Phoebe Hesketh has written a short poem about a picture that she likes (p. 110). Look carefully at the details of both. Can you pick out which details of the painting caught her eye?

Now look at Samuel Palmer's painting *Early Morning* (p. 113). List up to six details that you notice. Add a phrase or a comparison to each detail to describe it more fully. Then, using these notes, see if you can make a haiku or a short poem to go with the picture.

★ **Step into a picture.** Everyone will need to choose a picture of a country scene—a magazine photograph or a painting in a book —and bring it to the lesson. Try to choose a scene that it is easy to step into. First, on your own, concentrate hard on your picture until you imagine yourself actually *in* the landscape. What do you see? What do you hear? What do you feel? Jot down some notes —single words or phrases only.

Then, in pairs, show your picture to your partner and, using your notes, talk about what it was like inside the scene. You may notice details in the pictures that your partner has missed.

From your notes, write a rought draft about stepping inside your picture and swap with your partner. Work on the two bits of writing together to make two short poems.

Your poems and pictures could then form part of a classroom display.

Nonsense and Stuff

Mr Kartoffel

Mr Kartoffel's a whimsical man;
He drinks his beer from a watering-can,
And for no good reason that I can see
He fills his pockets with china tea.
He parts his hair with a knife and fork
And takes his ducks for a Sunday walk.
Says he, 'If my wife and I should choose
To wear our stockings outside our shoes,
Plant tulip-bulbs in the baby's pram
And eat tobacco instead of jam,
And fill the bath with cauliflowers,
That's nobody's business at all but ours.'
Says Mrs K., 'I may choose to travel
With a sack of grass or a sack of gravel,
Or paint my toes, one black, one white,
Or sit on a bird's nest half the night—
But whatever I do that is rum or rare,
I rather think that it's my affair.
So fill up your pockets with stamps and string,
And let us be ready for anything!'
Says Mr K. to his whimsical wife,
'How can we face the storms of life,
Unless we are ready for anything?
So if you've provided the stamps and the string,
Let us pump up the saddle and harness the horse
And fill him with carrots and custard and sauce,
Let us leap on him lightly and give him a shove
And it's over the sea and away, my love!'

JAMES REEVES

The Tale of Custard the Dragon

Belinda lived in a little white house,
With a little black kitten and a little gray mouse,
And a little yellow dog and a little red wagon,
And a realio, trulio, little pet dragon.

Now the name of the little black kitten was Ink,
And the little gray mouse, she called her Blink,
And the little yellow dog was sharp as Mustard,
But the dragon was a coward, and she called him Custard.

Custard the dragon had big sharp teeth,
And spikes on top of him and scales underneath,
Mouth like a fireplace, chimney for a nose,
And realio, trulio daggers on his toes.

Belinda was as brave as a barrel full of bears,
And Ink and Blink chased lions down the stairs,
Mustard was as brave as a tiger in a rage,
But Custard cried for a nice safe cage.

Belinda tickled him, she tickled him unmerciful,
Ink, Blink and Mustard they rudely called him Percival,
They all sat laughing in the little red wagon
At the realio, trulio cowardly dragon.

Belinda giggled till she shook the house,
And Blink said Weeck! which is giggling for a mouse,
Ink and Mustard rudely asked his age,
When Custard cried for a nice safe cage.

Suddenly, suddenly they heard a nasty sound,
And Mustard growled, and they all looked around.
Meowch! cried Ink, and Ooh! cried Belinda,
For there was a pirate climbing in the winda.

Pistol in his left hand, pistol in his right,
And he held in his teeth a cutlass bright,
His beard was black, one leg was wood;
It was clear that the pirate meant no good.

Belinda paled, and she cried Help! Help!
But Mustard fled with a terrified yelp,
Ink trickled down to the bottom of the household,
And little mouse Blink strategically mouseholed.

But up jumped Custard, snorting like an engine,
Clashed his tail like irons in a dungeon,
With a clatter and a clank and a jangling squirm
He went at the pirate like a robin at a worm.

The pirate gaped at Belinda's dragon,
And gulped some grog from his pocket flagon,
He fired two bullets, but they didn't hit,
And Custard gobbled him, every bit.

Belinda embraced him, Mustard licked him,
No one mourned for his pirate victim.
Ink and Blink in glee did gyrate
Around the dragon that ate the pyrate.

Belinda still lives in her little white house,
With her little black kitten and her little gray mouse,
And her little yellow dog and her little red wagon,
And her realio, trulio little pet dragon.

Belinda is as brave as a barrel full of bears,
And Ink and Blink chase lions down the stairs.
Mustard is as brave as a tiger in a rage,
But Custard keeps crying for a nice safe cage.

OGDEN NASH

The Song of the Jellicles

Jellicle Cats come out to-night,
Jellicle Cats come one come all:
The Jellicle Moon is shining bright—
Jellicles come to the Jellicle Ball.

Jellicle Cats are black and white,
Jellicle Cats are rather small;
Jellicle Cats are merry and bright,
And pleasant to hear when they caterwaul.
Jellicle Cats have cheerful faces,
Jellicle Cats have bright black eyes;
They like to practise their airs and graces
And wait for the Jellicle Moon to rise.

Jellicle Cats develop slowly,
Jellicle Cats are not too big;
Jellicle Cats are roly-poly,
They know how to dance a gavotte and a jig.
Until the Jellicle Moon appears
They make their toilette and take their repose:
Jellicles wash behind their ears,
Jellicles dry between their toes.

Jellicle Cats are white and black,
Jellicle Cats are of moderate size;
Jellicles jump like a jumping-jack,
Jellicle Cats have moonlit eyes.
They're quiet enough in the morning hours,
They're quiet enough in the afternoon,
Reserving their terpsichorean powers
To dance by the light of the Jellicle Moon.

Jellicle Cats are black and white,
Jellicle Cats (as I said) are small;
If it happens to be a stormy night
They will practise a caper or two in the hall.
If it happens the sun is shining bright

You would say they had nothing to do at all:
They are resting and saving themselves to be right
For the Jellicle Moon and the Jellicle Ball.

T. S. ELIOT

Macavity: The Mystery Cat

Macavity's a Mystery Cat: he's called the Hidden Paw—
For he's the master criminal who can defy the Law.
He's the bafflement of Scotland Yard, the Flying Squad's despair:
For when they reach the scene of crime—*Macavity's not there*!

Macavity, Macavity, there's no one like Macavity,
He's broken every human law, he breaks the law of gravity.
His powers of levitation would make a fakir stare,
And when you reach the scene of crime—*Macavity's not there*!
You may seek him in the basement, you may look up in the air—
But I tell you once and once again, *Macavity's not there*!

Macavity's a ginger cat, he's very tall and thin;
You would know him if you saw him, for his eyes are sunken in.
His brow is deeply lined with thought, his head is highly domed;
His coat is dusty from neglect, his whiskers are uncombed.
He sways his head from side to side, with movements like a snake;
And when you think he's half asleep, he's always wide awake.

Macavity, Macavity, there's no one like Macavity,
For he's a fiend in feline shape, a monster of depravity.
You may meet him in a by-street, you may see him in the square—
But when a crime's discovered, then *Macavity's not there*!

He's outwardly respectable. (They say he cheats at cards.)
And his footprints are not found in any file of Scotland
Yard's.
And when the larder's looted, or the jewel-case is rifled,
Or when the milk is missing, or another Peke's been stifled,
Or the greenhouse glass is broken, and the trellis past
repair—
Ay, there's the wonder of the thing! *Macavity's not there*!

And when the Foreign Office find a Treaty's gone astray,
Or the Admiralty lose some plans and drawings by the way,
There may be a scrap of paper in the hall or on the stair—
But it's useless to investigate—*Macavity's not there*!
And when the loss has been disclosed, the Secret Service
say:
'It *must* have been Macavity!'—but he's a mile away.
You'll be sure to find him resting, or a-licking of his thumbs,
Or engaged in doing complicated long division sums.

Macavity, Macavity, there's no one like Macavity,
There never was a Cat of such deceitfulness and suavity.
He always has an alibi, and one or two to spare:
At whatever time the deed took place—MACAVITY
WASN'T THERE!
And they say that all the Cats whose wicked deeds are
widely known
(I might mention Mungojerrie, I might mention
Griddlebone)
Are nothing more than agents for the Cat who all the time
Just controls their operations: the Napoleon of Crime!

T. S. ELIOT

The Common Cormorant

The common cormorant or shag
Lays eggs inside a paper bag.
The reason you will see no doubt
It is to keep the lightning out.
But what these unobservant birds
Have never noticed is that herds
Of wandering bears may come with buns
And steal the bags to hold the crumbs.

ANON.

The Walrus and the Carpenter

The sun was shining on the sea,
Shining with all his might:
He did his very best to make
The billows smooth and bright—
And this was odd, because it was
The middle of the night.

The moon was shining sulkily,
Because she thought the sun
Had got no business to be there
After the day was done—
'It's very rude of him,' she said,
'To come and spoil the fun.'

The sea was wet as wet could be,
The sands were dry as dry.
You could not see a cloud, because
No cloud was in the sky:
No birds were flying overhead—
There were no birds to fly.

The Walrus and the Carpenter
Were walking close at hand;
They wept like anything to see

Such quantities of sand:
'If this were only cleared away,'
They said, 'it *would* be grand!'

'If seven maids with seven mops
Swept it for half a year.
Do you suppose,' the Walrus said,
'That they could get it clear?'
'I doubt it,' said the Carpenter,
And shed a bitter tear.

'O Oysters, come and walk with us!'
The Walrus did beseech.
'A pleasant walk, a pleasant talk,
Along the briny beach:
We cannot do with more than four,
To give a hand to each.'

The eldest Oyster looked at him,
But never a word he said:
The eldest Oyster winked his eye,
And shook his heavy head—
Meaning to say he did not choose
To leave the oyster-bed.

But four young Oysters hurried up,
All eager for the treat:
Their coats were brushed, their faces washed,
Their shoes were clean and neat—
And this was odd, because, you know,
They hadn't any feet.

Four other Oysters followed them,
And yet another four;
And thick and fast they came at last,
And more, and more, and more—
All hopping through the frothy waves,
And scrambling to the shore.

The Walrus and the Carpenter
Walked on a mile or so,
And then they rested on a rock
Conveniently low:
And all the little Oysters stood
And waited in a row.

'The time has come,' the Walrus said,
'To talk of many things:
Of shoes—and ships—and sealing-wax—
Of cabbages—and kings—
And why the sea is boiling hot—
And whether pigs have wings.'

'But, wait a bit,' the Oysters cried,
'Before we have our chat:
For some of us are out of breath,
And all of us are fat!'
'No hurry!' said the Carpenter.
They thanked him much for that.

'A loaf of bread,' the Walrus said,
'Is what we chiefly need:
Pepper and vinegar besides
Are very good indeed—
Now if you're ready, Oysters dear,
We can begin to feed.'

'But not on us!' the Oysters cried,
Turning a little blue.
'After such kindness that would be
A dismal thing to do!'
'The night is fine,' the Walrus said,
'Do you admire the view?

'It was so kind of you to come:
And you are very nice!'
The Carpenter said nothing but,
'Cut us another slice:
I wish you were not quite so deaf—
I've had to ask you twice!'

'It seems a shame,' the Walrus said,
'To play them such a trick,
After we've brought them out so far,
And made them trot so quick!'

The Carpenter said nothing but,
'The butter's spread too thick.'

'I weep for you,' the Walrus said,
'I deeply sympathise.'
With sobs and tears he sorted out
Those of the largest size,
Holding his pocket-handkerchief
Before his streaming eyes.

'O Oysters,' said the Carpenter,
'You've had a pleasant run!
Shall we be trotting home again?'
But answer there was none—
And this was scarcely odd, because
They'd eaten every one.

LEWIS CARROLL

The Dong with a Luminous Nose

When awful darkness and silence reign
Over the great Gromboolian plain,
Through the long, long wintry nights;
When the angry breakers roar
As they beat on the rocky shore;
When Storm-clouds brood on the towering heights
Of the Hills of the Chankly Bore:
Then, through the vast and gloomy dark,
There moves what seems a fiery spark,
A lonely spark with silvery rays
Piercing the coal-black night,
A meteor strange and bright:
Hither and thither the vision strays,
A single lurid light.

Slowly it wanders,—pauses,—creeps,—
Anon it sparkles,—flashes and leaps;
And ever as onward it gleaming goes
A light on the Bong-tree stems it throws.
And those who watch at that midnight hour
From Hall or Terrace, or lofty Tower,
Cry, as the wild light passes along,—
'The Dong!—the Dong!
'The wandering Dong through the forest goes!
'The Dong! the Dong!
'The Dong with a luminous Nose!'

Long years ago
The Dong was happy and gay,
Till he fell in love with a Jumbly Girl
Who came to those shores one day.
For the Jumblies came in a Sieve, they did,—
Landing at eve near the Zemmery Fidd
Where the Oblong Oysters grow,
And the rocks are smooth and grey.
And all the woods and the valleys rang
With the Chorus they daily and nightly sang,—

'Far and few, far and few,
Are the lands where the Jumblies live;
Their heads are green, and their hands are blue,
And they went to sea in a Sieve.'

Happily, happily passed those days!
While the cheerful Jumblies stayed;
They danced in circlets all night long,
To the plaintive pipe of the lively Dong,
In moonlight, shine, or shade.
For day and night he was always there
By the side of the Jumbly Girl so fair,
With her sky-blue hands, and her sea-green hair,
Till the morning came of that hateful day
When the Jumblies sailed in their Sieve away,
And the Dong was left on the cruel shore—
Gazing—gazing for evermore,—
Ever keeping his weary eyes on
That pea-green sail on the far horizon,—
Singing the Jumbly Chorus still
As he sate all day on the grassy hill,—

'Far and few, far and few,
Are the lands where the Jumblies live;
Their heads are green, and their hands are blue,
And they went to sea in a Sieve.'

But when the sun was low in the West,
The Dong arose and said,—
'What little sense I once possessed
Has quite gone out of my head!'
And since that day he wanders still
By lake and forest, marsh and hill,
Singing—'O somewhere, in valley or plain
Might I find my Jumbly Girl again!
For ever I'll seek by lake and shore
Till I find my Jumbly Girl once more!'

Playing a pipe with silvery squeaks,
Since then his Jumbly Girl he seeks,
And because by night he could not see,
He gathered the bark of the Twangum Tree
On the flowery plain that grows.
And he wove him a wondrous Nose,—
A Nose as strange as a Nose could be!
Of vast proportions and painted red,
And tied with cords to the back of his head.
—In a hollow rounded space it ended
With a luminous lamp within suspended
All fenced about
With a bandage stout
To prevent the wind from blowing it out;
And with holes all round to send the light,
In gleaming rays on the dismal night.

And now each night, and all night long,
Over those plains still roams the Dong;
And above the wail of the Chimp and Snipe
You may hear the squeak of his plaintive pipe
While ever he seeks, but seeks in vain
To meet with his Jumbly Girl again;
Lonely and wild—all night he goes,—
The Dong with a luminous Nose!
And all who watch at the midnight hour,
From Hall or Terrace, or lofty Tower,
Cry, as they trace the Meteor bright,
Moving along through the dreary night,—
'This is the hour when forth he goes,
The Dong with a luminous Nose!
Yonder—over the plain he goes;
He goes!
He goes;
The Dong with a Luminous Nose!'

EDWARD LEAR

The Owl and the Pussy-cat

The Owl and the Pussy-cat went to sea
In a beautiful pea-green boat,
They took some honey, and plenty of money,
Wrapped up in a five-pound note.
The Owl looked up to the stars above,
And sang to a small guitar,
'O lovely Pussy! O Pussy, my love,
What a beautiful Pussy you are,
You are,
You are!
What a beautiful Pussy you are!'

Pussy said to the Owl, 'You elegant fowl!
How charmingly sweet you sing!
O let us be married! too long we have tarried,
But what shall we do for a ring?'

They sailed away for a year and a day,
To the land where the Bong-tree grows,
And there in a wood a Piggy-wig stood,
With a ring at the end of his nose,
His nose,
His nose,
With a ring at the end of his nose.

'Dear Pig, are you willing to sell for a shilling
Your ring?' Said the Piggy, 'I will.'
So they took it away, and were married next day
By the Turkey who lives on the hill.
They dined on mince, and slices of quince,
Which they ate with a runcible spoon;
And hand in hand, on the edge of the sand,
  They danced by the light of the moon,
    The moon,
    The moon,
  They danced by the light of the moon.

EDWARD LEAR

The Owl and the Astronaut

The owl and the astronaut
Sailed through space
In their intergalactic ship
They kept hunger at bay
With three pills a day
And drank through a protein drip.
The owl dreamed of mince
And slices of quince
And remarked how life had gone flat;
'It may be all right
To fly faster than light
But I preferred the boat and the cat.'

GARETH OWEN

Soldier Freddy

Soldier Freddy
was never ready,
But! Soldier Neddy,
unlike Freddy
Was *always* ready
and steady,

That's why,
When Soldier Neddy
Is-outside-Buckingham-Palace-on-guard-in-the pouring-
wind-and-rain-
being-steady-and-ready,
Freddy-
is home in beddy.

SPIKE MILLIGAN

Cousin Lesley's See-Through Stomach

Cousin Lesley took a pill
That made her go invisible.
Perhaps this would have been all right
If everything was out of sight.

But all around her stomach swam
Half-digested bread and jam,
And no matter how she tried
She couldn't hide what was inside.

In the morning we often noted
How the toast and porridge floated,
And how unappetizing in the light
Was the curry from last night.

Some Gruyère had fallen victim
To her strange digestive system,
And there seemed a million ways
To digest old mayonnaise.

We were often fascinated
By the stuff left undigested,
A mish-mash of peas and jelly
Drifted round our cousin's belly.

Certain bits of Cornish pastie
Looked repugnant and quite nasty,
While the strawberries from last year
Were without the cream, I fear.

And at dinner, oh dear me!
What a disgusting sight to see
Chewed-up fish and cold brown tea
Where Cousin Lesley's tum should be.

BRIAN PATTEN

Gust Becos I Cud Not Spel

Gust becos I cud not spel
It did not mean I was daft
When the boys in school red my riting
Some of them laffed

But now I am the dictater
They have to rite like me
Utherwise they cannot pas
Ther GCSE

Some of the girls wer ok
But those who laffed a lot
Have al bean rownded up
And hav recintly bean shot

The teecher who corrected my speling
As not been shot at al
But four the last fifteen howers
As bean standing up against a wal

He has to stand ther until he can spel
Figgymisgrugifooniyn the rite way
I think he will stand ther forever
I gust inventid it today

BRIAN PATTEN

★ **Performances.** Most nonsense and humorous poems are best spoken aloud. Here are some suggestions:

– *Mr Kartoffel* (p. 119). Three readers take the parts of the narrator and Mr and Mrs Kartoffel and rehearse a reading. Once you can speak the words fluently try to add simple movements to suggest some of the details.

– *The Song of the Jellicles* (p. 122). One or two voices might speak the four-line refrain at the start, and also repeat it after each section. Keep the same bouncy rhythm each time. For the rest, each line that begins 'Jellicle Cats . . .' should have a new voice; many readers will have just one line, others will have two or three. Either have a separate reader for the last six lines or share out these lines in pairs.

– *Macavity: The Mystery Cat* (p. 124). Seven readers take a verse each; all join in with 'Macavity's not there!'

– *The Owl and the Pussy-cat* (p. 134) and *The Owl and the Astronaut* (p. 137). Perform these as a pair. You'll need a narrator, an owl, a cat and a pig for the first poem; and a narrator and an owl for the second.

Several of the poems in this section can be shared among a number of voices. You may know other nonsense poems to add to this collection. Why not put together a spoken anthology to perform for a local junior school class or similar audience?

★ **Cartoons.** There are plenty of opportunities in these poems for cartoon illustrations:

– portraits of Mr and Mrs Kartoffel (p. 119)
– the characters in *The Tale of Custard the Dragon* (p. 120)
– two or three pictures of Macavity's crimes (p. 124)
– how *you* see the Dong and the Jumblies in Edward Lear's poem (p. 131). There are several details about their shape and colour in the poem. Make your drawing as bold and vivid as you can.
– the see-through stomach (p. 138)!

Working in pairs or small groups try to illustrate the poems in this section with your own drawings.

Sea

Across the Estuary

The fog floats in with the tide and lies on the mosses,
Branching up the channels like the veins on an old man's
hand.
The world of field and farm, the woods and the
embankment,
Are blurred away like figures on a slate.
Here, under the canvas of the fog,
Is only sand, and the dead, purple turf,
And gulleys in the mud where now the water
Thrusts flabby fingers. The wild geese
Feed beneath the mist, grey and still as sheep,
And cormorants curl black question-marks
Above the threshold of the sea.
Here is the track:
The ruts of cartwheels filled with water, the dark
Brogs* of broom. Unseen, a curlew calls—
A shadow slipping through the rippling mist;
Byzantine domes of foam sail up the gutters.
But now—where is the track? where are the ruts? The broom
Skulks back into the dark, and every footstep,
Dug deep in mud, draws water through the heels.
Each step goes wrong. Here, forward—deep, the sand
Shifts under foot like scree. Backward—deeper.
Stand still then—squids of sand
Wrap suckers round my feet. The tide
Tops the rim of the gulleys, and the mist
Tightens its cold, wet nets about my throat.

NORMAN NICHOLSON

*Note: In the days when the estuaries of Morecambe Bay and South Cumberland were crossed regularly by travellers on foot and by coach, the guides marked the track by planting branches of broom in the sands. This was called 'brogging the sands'.

Full Fathom Five

Full fathom five thy father lies;
  Of his bones are coral made;
Those are pearls that were his eyes:
  Nothing of him that doth fade,
But doth suffer a sea-change
Into something rich and strange.
Sea-nymphs hourly ring his knell:
      Ding-dong.
  Hark! now I hear them—
    Ding-dong, bell!

The Tempest, Act I, sc. ii
W. SHAKESPEARE

Drowning

Lord, Lord! methought, what pain it was to drown!
What dreadful noise of waters in mine ears!
What ugly sights of death within mine eyes!
Methought I saw a thousand fearful wrecks;
Ten thousand men that fishes gnaw'd upon;
Wedges of gold, great anchors, heaps of pearl,
Inestimable stones, unvalued jewels,
All scattered in the bottom of the sea:
Some lay in dead men's skulls; and in those holes
Where eyes did once inhabit, there were crept,
As 'twere in scorn of eyes, reflecting gems,
Which woo'd the slimy bottom of the deep,
And mock'd the dead bones that lay scattered by.

Richard III, Act I, sc. iv
W. SHAKESPEARE

Seaside Serenade

It begins when you smell a funny smell,
And it isn't vanilla or caramel,
And it isn't forget-me-nots or lilies,
Or new-mown hay, or daffy-down-dillies,
And it's not what the barber rubs on Father,
And it's awful, and yet you like it rather.
No, it's not what the barber rubs on Daddy,
It's more like an elderly finnan haddie,
Or, shall we say, an electric fan
Blowing over a sardine can.
It's as fishy as millions of fishy fishes,
In spite of which you find it delishes,
You could do with a second helping, please,
And that, my dears, is the ocean breeze.
And pretty soon you observe a pack
Of people reclining upon their back,
And another sight that is very common
Is people reclining upon their abdomen.
And now you lose the smell of the ocean
In the sweetish vapour of sunburn lotion,
And the sun itself seems paler and colder,
Compared to vermilion face and shoulder.
Athletic young men uncover their torso
In the virile way that maidens adore so,
While paunchy uncles, before they bathe them,
In voluminous beach robes modestly swathe them.
The beach is peppered with ladies who look
Like pictures out of a medical book.
Last, not least, consider the kiddies,
Chirping like crickets and katydiddies,
Splashing, squealing, slithering, crawling,
Cheerful, tearful, boisterous, bawling,
Kiddies in clamorous crowds that swarm
Heavily over your prostrate form,
Kiddies who bring, as a priceless cup,
Something dead that a wave washed up.
Oh, I must go down to the beach, my lass,
And step on a piece of broken glass.

OGDEN NASH

A Sailor Sat on the Watery Shore

A sailor sat on the watery shore
  By the side of the shiny sea,
And as the billows railed and roared
  These words he said to me.
'I've sailed to the Rock from Plymouth Dock
  And from Sydney to Simonstown,
And oh but it's true that a life on the blue
  Ain't the same as the life on the brown.

'For there's gusts and there's gales and there's spirting
  whales
  And there's fish flying round like a fountain,
And there's bays and there's bights and there's Great
  Northern Lights,
  And there's oceans as deep as a mountain.
And then there's your mates in the varying states
  From the angel and saint to the sinner,
Though I think you will find they are much of a kind
  When you sit down beside 'em for dinner.

'And yarns by the fathom you'll hear 'em all spin
  Of ghost-ships and sea-serpents mighty,
Of mermaids divine, and of Crossing the Line
  With King Neptune and Queen Amphitrite.
O many the lays I could sing of the days
  As in suits dazzling white from the dhoby*   *the wash*
We sauntered ashore in New York, Singapore,
  Or went up the line to Nairobi.

'And your eyes, my young friend, would jump out of your
  head,
  When the ship bade old England good-bye-ee,
At the antics of tars to the sound of guitars
  Whether strummed in Cadiz or Hawaii.
You may search the world through, but no friend is as true
  As the matelot so trim and stout-hearted,
Though when he comes on leave (and to tell it, I grieve)
  There's no man from his pay sooner parted.

'Furthermore,' said the sailor, 'it's certain to me
  As this beach is all covered with sand,
Though a sailor may find many sharks in the sea
  He will find even more on the land.'
'Ah, sailor,' I said, 'but I feel that your heart
  For the world of the wave is still yearning,
And I think I surmise from the look in your eyes
  That to it you'll soon be returning.'

'Good gracious!' the sailor said. 'Certainly not,
  And I can't think what gave you the notion
That once having left it, I'd wish to return
  To the dark, unpredictable ocean.
I've a nice little semi in Citadel Road
  That faces away from the sea,
And the reason it's thus—but, dear me, there's my bus
  And it's time for my afternoon tea!'

CHARLES CAUSLEY

The *Revenge*

At Florés in the Azores Sir Richard Grenville lay,
And a pinnace, like a fluttered bird, came flying from far
  away:
'Spanish ships of war at sea! we have sighted fifty-three!'
Then sware Lord Thomas Howard: ''Fore God I am no
  coward;
But I cannot meet them here, for my ships are out of gear,
And the half my men are sick. I must fly, but follow quick.
We are six ships of the line; can we fight with fifty-three?'

Then spake Sir Richard Grenville: 'I know you are no
  coward;
You fly them for a moment to fight with them again.
But I've ninety men and more that are lying sick ashore.
I should count myself the coward if I left them, my Lord
  Howard,
To these Inquisition dogs and the devildoms of Spain.'

So Lord Howard passed away with five ships of war that
  day,
Till he melted like a cloud in the silent summer heaven;
But Sir Richard bore in hand all his sick men from the land
Very carefully and slow,
Men of Bideford in Devon,
And we laid them on the ballast down below;
For we brought them all aboard,
And they blest him in their pain, that they were not left to
  Spain,
To the thumbscrew and the stake, for the glory of the Lord.

He had only a hundred seamen to work the ship and to fight,
And he sailed away from Florés till the Spaniard came in
  sight,
With his huge sea-castles heaving upon the weather bow.
'Shall we fight or shall we fly?
Good Sir Richard, tell us now,
For to fight is but to die!

There'll be little of us left by the time this sun be set.'
And Sir Richard said again: 'We be all good English men.
Let us bang these dogs of Seville, the children of the devil,
For I never turned my back upon Don or devil yet.'

Sir Richard spoke and he laughed, and we roared a hurrah,
and so
The little *Revenge* ran on sheer into the heart of the foe,
With her hundred fighters on deck, and her ninety sick
below;
For half their fleet to the right and half to the left were seen,
And the little *Revenge* ran on through the long sea-lane
between.

Thousands of their soldiers looked down from their decks
and laughed,
Thousands of their seamen made mock at the mad little craft
Running on and on, till delayed
By their mountain-like *San Philip* that, of fifteen hundred
tons,
And up-shadowing high above us with her yawning tiers of
guns,
Took the breath from our sails, and we stayed.

And while now the great *San Philip* hung above us like a
cloud
Whence the thunderbolt will fall
Long and loud,
Four galleons drew away
From the Spanish fleet that day,
And two upon the larboard and two upon the starboard lay,
And the battle thunder broke from them all.

But anon the great *San Philip*, she bethought herself and
went,
Having that within her womb that had left her ill content;
And the rest they came aboard us, and they fought us hand
to hand,

For a dozen times they came, with their pikes and
musqueteers,
And a dozen times we shook 'em off as a dog that shakes his
ears
When he leaps from the water to the land.

And the sun went down, and the stars came out far over the
summer sea,
But never a moment ceased the fight of the one and the
fifty-three.
Ship after ship, the whole night long, their high-built
galleons came,
Ship after ship, the whole night long, with her
battle-thunder and flame;
Ship after ship, the whole night long, drew back with her
dead and her shame.
For some were sunk and many were shattered, and so could
fight us no more—
God of battles, was ever a battle like this in the world before?

For he said, 'Fight on! Fight on!'
Though his vessel was all but a wreck;
And it chanced that, when half of the short summer night
  was gone,
With a grisly wound to be drest he had left the deck,
But a bullet struck him that was dressing it suddenly dead,
And himself he was wounded again in the side and the
  head,
And he said, 'Fight on! fight on!'

And the night went down and the sun smiled out far over
  the summer sea,
And the Spanish fleet with broken sides lay around us all in a
  ring;
But they dared not touch us again, for they feared that we
  still could sting,
So they watched what the end would be.

And we had not fought them in vain,
But in perilous plight were we,
Seeing forty of our poor hundred were slain,
And half the rest of us maimed for life
In the crash of the cannonades and the desperate strife;
And the sick men down in the hold were most of them stark
  and cold,
And the pikes were all broken or bent, and the powder was
  all of it spent;
And the masts and the rigging were lying over the side;
But Sir Richard cried in his English pride,
'We have fought such a fight for a day and a night,
As may never be fought again!
We have won great glory, my men!
And a day less or more
At sea or ashore,
We die—does it matter when?
Sink me the ship, Master Gunner—sink her, split her in
  twain!
Fall into the hands of God, not into the hands of Spain!'

And the gunner said, 'Ay, Ay,' but the seamen made reply:
'We have children, we have wives,
And the Lord hath spared our lives.
We will make the Spaniard promise, if we yield, to let us go;
We shall live to fight again and to strike another blow.'
And the lion there lay dying, and they yielded to the foe.

And the stately Spanish men to their flagship bore him then,
Where they laid him by the mast, old Sir Richard caught at
last,
And they praised him to his face with their courtly foreign
grace;
But he rose upon their decks, and he cried:
'I have fought for Queen and Faith like a valiant man and
true;
I have only done my duty as a man is bound to do;
With a joyful spirit I Sir Richard Grenville die!'
And he fell upon their decks, and he died.

And they stared at the dead that had been so valiant and true,
And had holden the power and glory of Spain so cheap
That he dared her with one little ship and his English few;
Was he devil or man? He was devil for aught they knew,
But they sank his body with honour down into the deep,
And they manned the *Revenge* with a swarthier alien crew,
And away she sailed with her loss and longed for her own;
When a wind from the lands they had ruined awoke from sleep,
And the water began to heave and the weather to moan,
And or ever that evening ended a great gale blew,
And a wave like the wave that is raised by an earthquake grew,
Till it smote on their hulls and their sails and their masts and
  their flags
And the whole sea plunged and fell on the shot-shattered
  navy of Spain,
And the little *Revenge* herself went down by the island crags
To be lost evermore in the main.

LORD TENNYSON

Cargoes

Quinquireme of Nineveh from distant Ophir
Rowing home to haven in sunny Palestine,
  With a cargo of ivory,
  And apes and peacocks,
Sandalwood, cedarwood, and sweet white wine.

Stately Spanish galleon coming from the Isthmus,
Dipping through the Tropics by the palm-green shores,
  With a cargo of diamonds,
  Emeralds, amethysts,
Topazes, and cinnamon, and gold moidores.

Dirty British coaster with a salt-caked smoke stack
Butting through the Channel in the mad March days,
  With a cargo of Tyne coal,
  Road rail, pig-lead,
Firewood, iron-ware, and cheap tin trays.

JOHN MASEFIELD

Thoughts like an Ocean

The sea comes to me on the shore
On lacy slippered feet
And shyly, slyly slides away
With a murmur of defeat.

And as I stand there wondering
Strange thoughts spin round my head
Of why and where and what and when
And if not, why, what then?

Where do lobsters come from?
And where anemones?
And are there other worlds out there
With other mysteries?

Why do *I* walk upon dry land
While fishes haunt the sea?
And as I think about their lives
Do they too think of me?

Why is water, water?
Why does it wet my hand?
Are there really as many stars
As there are grains of sand?

And where would the ocean go to
If there were no gravity?
And where was I before I lived?
And where's eternity?

Perhaps the beach I'm standing on
Perhaps this stretch of sand
Perhaps the Universe itself
Lies on someone else's hand?

And isn't it strange how this water and I
At this moment happened to meet?
And how this tide sweeps half the world
Before stopping at my feet?

GARETH OWEN

maggie and milly and molly and may

maggie and milly and molly and may
went down to the beach (to play one day)

and maggie discovered a shell that sang
so sweetly she couldn't remember her troubles,and

milly befriended a stranded star
whose rays five languid fingers were;

and molly was chased by a horrible thing
which raced sideways while blowing bubbles:and

may came home with a smooth round stone
as small as a world and as large as alone.

For whatever we lose(like a you or a me)
it's always ourselves we find in the sea

e. e. cummings

The Main-Deep

The long-rolling,
Steady-póuring
Deep-trenchéd
Green billów:

 The wide-topped,
Unbróken,
Green-glacid,
Slow-sliding,

 Cold-flushing,
—On—on—on—
Chill-rushing,
 Hush-hushing,

. . . Hush-hushing . . .

JAMES STEPHENS

Tell Me, Tell Me, Sarah Jane

Tell me, tell me, Sarah Jane,
  Tell me, dearest daughter,
Why are you holding in your hand
  A thimbleful of water?
Why do you hold it to your eye
  And gaze both late and soon
From early morning light until
  The rising of the moon?

Mother, I hear the mermaids cry,
  I hear the mermen sing,
And I can see the sailing-ships
  All made of sticks and string.
And I can see the jumping fish,
  The whales that fall and rise
And swim about the waterspout
  That swarms up to the skies.

Tell me, tell me, Sarah Jane,
  Tell your darling mother,
Why do you walk beside the tide
  As though you loved none other?
Why do you listen to a shell
  And watch the billows curl,
And throw away your diamond ring
  And wear instead the pearl?

Mother I hear the water
  Beneath the headland pinned,
And I can see the seagull
  Sliding down the wind.
I taste the salt upon my tongue
  As sweet as sweet can be.

Tell me, my dear, whose voice you hear?

  It is the sea, the sea.

CHARLES CAUSLEY

★ **Beachcombing.** Think back to the last time you were at the seaside. Perhaps you collected shells, coloured stones, driftwood ... In pairs, talk about what you have found. Now, on your own, focus on one or two objects. Look at the details and think about the way in which the sea has changed them. Write and illustrate a poem about your chosen object.

★ **Haiku.** Focus on *one* seaside picture in your mind's eye and capture it as a 'snapshot' in seventeen syllables (see pp. 3–6). If a comparison comes to mind, all the better. Here are a few ideas, but choose your own if you can: pools in the rocks; sand-dunes; maps and charts; wind-surfers; a lighthouse; breakwaters; watching the sea engulfing a sand-castle; sea-birds round a cliff; the pier or promenade; a crowded beach on a public holiday. If you choose the last idea, the picture on p. 144 might help you.

★ **Undersea tableau.** The *Mary Rose*, the *Titanic* . . . these and other wrecks have been raised or photographed in recent years. Perhaps you have visited or read about the *Mary Rose* or seen television programmes about underwater explorations. Look at the poems and picture on pp. 142–3. Hear the poems read aloud. Working in a small group, design a tableau of poems and pictures to create the atmosphere of under the sea. You might include: illustrated copies of the two poems on pp. 142–3; pictures of the *Mary Rose* or other wrecks; your own poems about these pictures . . .

★ **Performances.** Three of the last poems in this section, read in sequence by different voices, make a quietly effective performance, either live or taped. You could arrange your readers as follows:

- *Thoughts like an Ocean*: one reader for verses 1, 2, 7 and 8; separate voices for each of the other verses.
- *Maggie and Milly* . . .: one reader for the first and last verses; separate voices for each of the four girls in verses 2–5.
- *Tell Me, Tell Me, Sarah Jane*: shared between the two voices of the mother and daughter.

People and Places

LIZZIE

When I was eleven
there was Lizzie.
I used to think this:

You don't care, Lizzie,
you say
that you're a ginger-nut
and you don't care.

I've noticed
that they try to soften you up

they say
you're clumsy

they say
you can't wear shorts
to school

but you say,
'I don't care,
I mean
how can I play football
in a skirt?'

Lizzie,
I'm afraid of saying
I think you're great

because, you see,
the teachers call you
tomboy.

I'm sorry
but I make out, as if
I agree with the teachers

and the other girls
wear bracelets
and I've noticed
they don't shout like you
or whistle,
and, you see,
the other boys
are always talking about
those girls
with the bracelets

So I do too.

So I know
that makes me a coward
but that's why I don't dare
to say you're great,

but I think it to myself
when you're there
but I don't say.

I just try to show
I like you
by laughing
and joking about
and pulling mad faces.

I'm sorry
but I don't suppose
you'll ever know . . .

MICHAEL ROSEN

Childhood

I used to think that grown-up people chose
To have stiff backs and wrinkles round their nose,
And veins like small fat snakes on either hand,
On purpose to be grand.
Till through the banisters I watched one day
My great-aunt Etty's friend who was going away,
And how her onyx beads had come unstrung.
I saw her grope to find them as they rolled;
And then I knew that she was helplessly old,
As I was helplessly young.

FRANCES CORNFORD

The Mad Woman

As well within her billowed skirts
Like a great ship with sails unfurled,
The mad woman goes gallantly
Upon the ridges of her world.

With eagle nose and wisps of gray
She strides upon the westward hills,
Swings her umbrella joyously
And waves it to the waving mills,

Talking and chuckling as she goes
Indifferent both to sun and rain,
With all that merry company,
The singing children of her brain.

L. A. G. STRONG

Growing up

I know a lad called Billy
Who goes along with me
He plays this game
Where he uses my name
And makes people think that he's me.

Don't ever mess with Billy
He's a vicious sort of bloke
He'll give you a clout
For saying nowt
And thump you for a joke.

My family can't stand Billy
Can't bear him round the place
He won't eat his food
He's rough and rude
And wears scowls all over his face.

No one can ever break Billy
He's got this look in his eye
That seems to say
You can wale*me all day
But you'll not make Billy cry.

He has a crazy face has Billy
Eyes that look but can't see
A mouth like a latch
Ears that don't match
And a space where his brain should be.

Mad Billy left one morning
Crept away without being seen
Left his body for me
That fits perfectly
And a calm where his madness had been.

GARETH OWEN

beat

Mrs Malone

Mrs Malone
Lived hard by a wood
All on her lonesome
As nobody should.
With her crust on a plate
And her pot on the coal
And none but herself
To converse with, poor soul.
In a shawl and a hood
She got sticks out-o'-door,
On a bit of old sacking
She slept on the floor,
And nobody, nobody
Asked how she fared
Or knew how she managed,
For nobody cared.
    Why make a pother
    About an old crone?
    What for should they bother
    With Mrs Malone?

One Monday in winter
With snow on the ground
So thick that a footstep
Fell without sound,
She heard a faint frostbitten
Peck on the pane
And went to the window
To listen again.
There sat a cock-sparrow

Bedraggled and weak,
With half-open eyelid
And ice on his beak.
She threw up the sash
And she took the bird in,
And mumbled and fumbled it
Under her chin.
'Ye're all of a smother,
Ye're fair overblown!
I've room fer another,'
Said Mrs Malone.

Come Tuesday while eating
Her dry morning slice
With the sparrow a-picking
('Ain't company nice!')
She heard on her doorpost
A curious scratch,
And there was a cat
With its claw on the latch.
It was hungry and thirsty
And thin as a lath,
It mewed and it mowed
On the slithery path.
She threw the door open
And warmed up some pap,
And huddled and cuddled it
In her old lap.
'There, there, little brother,
Ye poor skin-an'-bone,
There's room fer another,'
Said Mrs Malone.

Come Wednesday while all of them
Crouched on the mat
With a crumb for the sparrow,
A sip for the cat,
There was wailing and whining
Outside in the wood,

And there sat a vixen
With six of her brood.
She was haggard and ragged
And worn to a shred,
And her half-dozen babies
Were only half-fed,
But Mrs Malone, crying
'My! ain't they sweet!'
Happed them and lapped them
And gave them to eat.
'You warm yerself, mother,
Ye're cold as a stone!
There's room fer another,'
Said Mrs Malone.

Come Thursday a donkey
Stepped in off the road
With sores on his withers
From bearing a load.
Come Friday when icicles
Pierced the white air
Down from the mountainside
Lumbered a bear.
For each she had something,
If little, to give—
'Lord knows, the poor critters
Must all of 'em live.'
She gave them her sacking,
Her hood and her shawl,
Her loaf and her teapot—
She gave them her all.
'What with one thing and t'other
Me fambily's grown,
And there's room fer another,'
Said Mrs Malone.

Come Saturday evening
When time was to sup
Mrs Malone

Had forgot to sit up.
The cat said *meeow,*
And the sparrow said *peep,*
The vixen, *she's sleeping,*
The bear, *let her sleep.*
On the back of the donkey
They bore her away,
Through trees and up mountains
Beyond night and day,
Till come Sunday morning
They brought her in state
Through the last cloudbank
As far as the Gate.
'Who is it,' asked Peter,
You have with you there?'
And donkey and sparrow,
Cat, vixen and bear

Exclaimed, 'Do you tell us
Up here she's unknown?
It's our mother, God bless us!
It's Mrs Malone
Whose havings were few
And whose holding was small
And whose heart was so big
It had room for us all.'
Then Mrs Malone
Of a sudden awoke,
She rubbed her two eyeballs
And anxiously spoke:
'Where am I, to goodness,
And what do I see?
My dears, let's turn back,
This ain't no place fer me!'
But Peter said, 'Mother
Go in to the Throne.
There's room for another
One, Mrs Malone.'

ELEANOR FARJEON

My Dad, Your Dad

My dad's fatter than your dad,
Yes, my dad's fatter than yours:
If he eats any more he won't fit in the house,
He'll have to live out of doors.

Yes, but my dad's balder than your dad,
My dad's balder, OK,
He's only got two hairs left on his head
And both are turning grey.

Ah, but my dad's thicker than your dad,
My dad's thicker, all right.
He has to look at his watch to see
If it's noon or the middle of the night.

Yes, but my dad's more boring than your dad.
If he ever starts counting sheep
When he can't get to sleep at night, he finds
It's the sheep that go to sleep.

But my dad doesn't mind your dad.
Mine quite likes yours too.
I suppose they don't always think much of US!
That's true, I suppose, that's true.

KIT WRIGHT

The Lesson

A poem that raises the question:
Should there be capital punishment in schools?

Chaos ruled OK in the classroom
as bravely the teacher walked in
the nooligans ignored him
his voice was lost in the din

'The theme for today is violence
and homework will be set
I'm going to teach you a lesson
one that you'll never forget'

He picked on a boy who was shouting
and throttled him then and there
then garrotted the girl behind him
(the one with grotty hair)

Then sword in hand he hacked his way
between the chattering rows
'First come, first severed' he declared
'fingers, feet, or toes'

He threw the sword at a latecomer
it struck with deadly aim
then pulling out a shotgun
he continued with his game

The first blast cleared the backrow
(where those who skive hang out)
they collapsed like rubber dinghies
when the plug's pulled out

'Please may I leave the room sir?'
a trembling vandal enquired
'Of course you may' said teacher
put the gun to his temple and fired

The Head popped a head round the doorway
to see why a din was being made
nodded understandingly
then tossed in a grenade

And when the ammo was well spent
with blood on every chair
Silence shuffled forward
with its hands up in the air

The teacher surveyed the carnage
the dying and the dead
He waggled a finger severely
'Now let that be a lesson' he said

ROGER McGOUGH

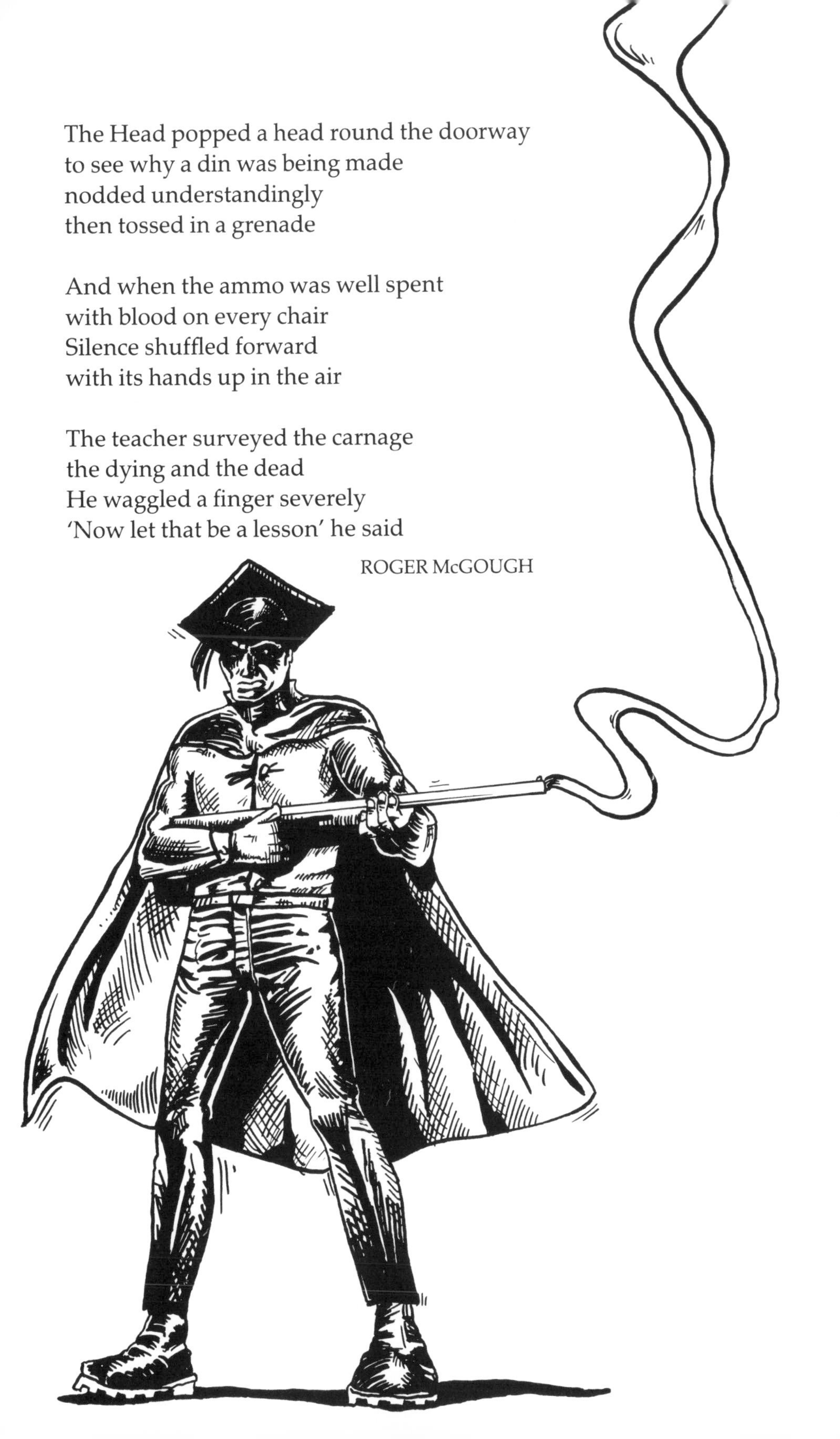

Watch Your French

When my mum tipped a panful of red-hot fat
Over her foot, she did quite a little chat,
And I won't tell you what she said
But it wasn't:
'Fancy that!
I must try in future to be far more careful
With this red-hot scalding fat!'

When my dad fell over and landed—splat!—
With a trayful of drinks (he'd tripped over the cat)
I won't tell you what he said
But it wasn't:
'Fancy that!
I must try in future to be far more careful
To step *round* our splendid cat!'

When Uncle Joe brought me a cowboy hat
Back from the States, the dog stomped it flat,
And I won't tell you what I said
But Mum and Dad yelled:
'STOP THAT!
Where did you learn that appalling language?
Come on. Where?'
'I've no idea,' I said,
'No idea.'

KIT WRIGHT

Excuses

I've writ on the wrong page, Miss,
My pencil went all blunt.
My book was upside-down, Miss,
My book was back to front.

My margin's gone all crooked, Miss,
I've smudged mine with my scarf.
I've rubbed a hole in the paper, Miss,
My ruler's broke in half.

My work's blew out the window, Miss,
My work's fell in the bin.
The leg's dropped off my chair, Miss,
The ceiling's coming in.

I've ate a poison apple, Miss,
I've held a poison pen!
I think I'm being *kidnapped*, Miss!
So... can we start again?

Allan Ahlberg

Seven Ages of Man

All the world's a stage,
And all the men and women merely players;
They have their exits and their entrances,
And one man in his time plays many parts,
His acts being seven ages. At first the infant,
Mewling* and puking in the nurse's arms: *crying feebly*
And then the whining schoolboy, with his satchel
And shining morning face, creeping like snail
Unwillingly to school. And then the lover,
Sighing like furnace, with a woeful ballad
Made to his mistress' eyebrow. Then, a soldier,
Full of strange oaths, and bearded like the pard,* *leopard*
Jealous in honour, sudden and quick in quarrel,
Seeking the bubble reputation
Even in the cannon's mouth. And then, the justice,
In fair round belly, with good capon* lin'd, *young chicken*
With eyes severe and beard of formal cut,
Full of wise saws,* and modern instances, *sayings*
And so he plays his part. The sixth age shifts
Into the lean and slipper'd pantaloon,* *foolish old man*
With spectacles on nose, and pouch on side,
His youthful hose well sav'd, a world too wide
For his shrunk shank;* and his big manly voice, *leg*
Turning again toward childish treble, pipes
And whistles in his sound. Last scene of all,
That ends this strange eventful history,
Is second childishness and mere oblivion;* *nothingness*
Sans* teeth, sans eyes, sans taste, sans every thing. *without*

As You Like It, Act II, sc. vii
W. SHAKESPEARE

The Miller

THE MILLERE was a stout carl for the nones;
Full byg he was of brawn, and eek of bones.
That proved wel, for over al ther he cam,
At wrastlynge he wolde have alwey the ram.
He was short-sholdred, brood, a thikke knarre;
Ther was no dore that he nolde heve of harre,
Or breke it at a rennying with his heed.
His berd as any sowe or fox was reed,
And therto brood, as though it were a spade.
Upon the cop right of his nose he hade
A werte, and theron stood a toft of herys,
Reed as the brustles of a sowes erys;
His nosethirles blake were and wyde.
A swerd and bokeler bar he by his syde.
His mouth as greet was as a greet forneys.
He was a janglere and a goliardeys,
And that was moost of synne and harlotries.
Wel koude he stelen corn and tollen thries;
And yet he hadde a thombe of gold,pardee.
A whit cote and a blew hood wered he.
A baggepipe well koude he blowe and sowne,
And therwithal he broghte us out of towne.

from the *General Prologue* to the
Canterbury Tales
GEOFFREY CHAUCER

The Miller

A Modern Translation

The miller was an exceedingly strong fellow;
He was very muscular and heavy-boned.
That was evident enough for wherever he went
He would always win the prize of a ram for wrestling.
He was a thickset, broad and sturdy fellow;
There was no door that he could not heave off its hinges,
Or break by running at it with his head.
His beard was red like the hairs of a sow or a fox,
And was also broad and shaped like a spade.
Right at the tip of his nose he had
A wart on which stood a tuft of hairs
Red as the bristles of a sow's ears;
His nostrils were black and wide.
He bore a sword and buckler at his side.
His mouth was as great as a furnace.
He was loud-mouthed and a coarse joker
And talked mostly about sin and wickedness.
He was good at stealing corn and at taking three times his
   legal payment;
And yet he was honest as millers go.
He wore a white coat and a blue hood.
He could perform well on the bagpipes
And he played us out of town.

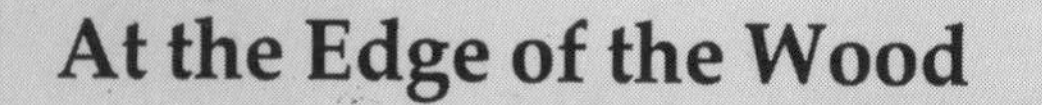

At the Edge of the Wood

First, boys out of school went out of their way home
To detonate the windows; at each smash
Piping with delight and skipping for fright
Of a ghost of the old man popping over his hedge,
Shrieking and nodding from the gate.
Then the game palled, since it was only breaking the silence.
The rain sluiced through the starred gaps,
Crept up walls into the brick; frost bit and munched;
Weeds craned in and leant on the doors.
Now it is a plot without trees let into the wood
Piled high with tangle and tousle
Buried parapets and roots picking at the last mortar
Though the chimney still stands sheathed in leaves
And you can see for the time being where in a nook
A briony burst its pot with a shower of roots
And back through the press of shrubs and stems
Deep-coils into the woods.

PETER REDGROVE

Stopping by Woods on a Snowy Evening

Whose woods these are I think I know.
His house is in the village though;
He will not see me stopping here
To watch his woods fill up with snow.

My little horse must think it queer
To stop without a farmhouse near
Between the woods and frozen lake
The darkest evening of the year.

He gives his harness bells a shake
To ask if there is some mistake.
The only other sound's the sweep
Of easy wind and downy flake.

The woods are lovely, dark and deep,
But I have promises to keep,
And miles to go before I sleep,
And miles to go before I sleep.

ROBERT FROST

The Way through the Woods

They shut the road through the woods
Seventy years ago.
Weather and rain have undone it again,
And now you would never know
There was once a road through the woods
Before they planted the trees.
It is underneath the coppice and heath
And the thin anemones.
Only the keeper sees
That, where the ring-dove broods,
And the badgers roll at ease,
There was once a road through the woods.

Yet, if you enter the woods
Of a summer evening late,
When the night-air cools on the trout-ringed pools
Where the otter whistles his mate,
(They fear not men in the woods,
Because they see so few)
You will hear the beat of a horse's feet,
And the swish of a skirt in the dew,
Steadily cantering through
The misty solitudes,
As thought they perfectly knew
The old lost road through the woods . . .
But there is no road through the woods.

RUDYARD KIPLING

Child on top of a Greenhouse

The wind billowing out the seat of my britches,
My feet crackling splinters of glass and dried putty,
The half-grown chrysanthemums staring up like accusers,
Up through the streaked glass, flashing with sunlight,
A few white clouds all rushing eastward,
A line of elms plunging and tossing like horses,
And everyone, everyone pointing up and shouting!

THEODORE ROETHKE

Snow in the Suburbs

Every branch big with it,
Bent every twig with it;
Every fork like a white web-foot;
Every street and pavement mute:
Some flakes have lost their way, and grope back upward, when
Meeting those meandering down they turn and descend again.
The palings are glued together like a wall,
And there is no waft of wind with the fleecy fall.

A sparrow enters the tree,
Whereon immediately
A snow-lump thrice his own slight size
Descends on him and showers his head and eyes.
And overturns him,
And near inurns him,
And lights on a nether twig, when its brush
Starts off a volley of other lodging lumps with a rush.

The steps are a blanched slope,
Up which, with feeble hope,
A black cat comes, wide-eyed and thin;
And we take him in.

THOMAS HARDY

★ **Storyboard.** First, hear the poem *Mrs Malone* (p. 163) read aloud. The idea then is to prepare a live reading of the poem against the background of a series of nine pictures—one for each of the days of the week, plus a title picture for the first section and a final picture as Mrs Malone enters heaven. Groups of three draw and colour your pictures, using sugar paper and either felt tips or paints. Your aim is to make a frieze along one wall of the classroom. When this is complete, rehearse a reading of the poem. Each group is responsible for speaking its particular section and sharing out the lines as seems appropriate.

★ **Performances.** The two easiest poems to speak aloud are:

– *My Dad, Your Dad* (p. 167): shared between the two children's voices; and

– *Excuses* (p. 171): read one line per person, perhaps with your teacher taking the last one.

Two more difficult ones are:

– *Seven Ages of Man* (p. 172): first, listen to the poem read aloud; then in groups of four, read it through and make sure you understand the eight parts—the opening lines and the seven 'ages' that follow. Then, perhaps taking two parts per group, prepare a reading of the poem.

– *The Miller* (pp. 174 and 175): this is one for individuals to rehearse and read aloud for the rest of the class. You can get the sense of the original Chaucer with help from the modern translation opposite. Don't be frightened of making the wrong sounds—you can't learn to play an instrument without hitting a few wrong notes! As a rough guide, 'a' sounds are often flat—'w*a*s', 'wr*a*stlynge'; and the final 'e' is often pronounced —'wold*e*', 'thikk*e*'. Have a go! If you want to hear how Chaucer's English sounds, listen to the cassette, *Prologue to the Canterbury Tales*, Argo.

★ **Picture into poem.** Look carefully at the picture on p. 183. Make a list of the details you notice about the clown and the showground. Jot down some words or phrases to describe the mood of the picture. Think how this mood might change when the clown is performing his act. Using your notes, write a short poem called 'The Clown'.

Witchcraft, Magic and Mystery

The Witches' Chant

A Cavern: in the middle, a boiling cauldron.
Thunder. Enter the three witches.

1st Witch Thrice the brinded cat hath mew'd.
2nd Witch Thrice, and once the hedge-pig whin'd.
3rd Witch Harpier cries, ''Tis time, 'tis time.'
1st Witch Round about the cauldron go:
In the poisoned entrails throw;
Toad, that under cold stone
Days and nights has thirty one
Swelter'd venom sleeping got,
Boil thou first i' th' charmed pot.
All Double, double, toil and trouble;
Fire burn, and cauldron bubble.
2nd Witch Fillet of a fenny snake,
In the cauldron boil and bake;
Eye of newt, and toe of frog,
Wool of bat, and tongue of dog;
Adder's fork, and blind-worm's sting,
Lizard's leg, and howlet's wing;
For a charm of powerful trouble,
Like a hell-broth, boil and bubble.
All Double, double, toil and trouble,
Fire burn, and cauldron bubble.
3rd Witch Scale of dragon, tooth of wolf,
Witches' mummy, maw, and gulf

Of the ravin'd salt-sea shark;
Root of hemlock, digg'd i' th' dark;
Liver of blaspheming Jew,
Gall of goat, and slips of yew,
Sliver'd in the moon's eclipse;
Nose of Turk, and Tartar's lips;
Finger of birth-strangled babe,
Ditch-deliver'd by a drab,
Make the gruel thick and slab;
Add thereto a tiger's chaudron,
For the ingredients of our cauldron.

All Double, double, toil and trouble,
Fire burn, and cauldron bubble.

Macbeth, Act IV, sc. i
W. SHAKESPEARE

The Listeners

'Is there anybody there?' said the Traveller,
Knocking on the moonlit door;
And his horse in the silence champed the grasses
Of the forest's ferny floor:
And a bird flew up out of the turret,
Above the Traveller's head:
And he smote upon the door again a second time;
'Is there anybody there?' he said.
But no one descended to the Traveller;
No head from the leaf-fringed sill
Leaned over and looked into his grey eyes,
Where he stood perplexed and still.
But only a host of phantom listeners
That dwelt in the lone house then
Stood listening in the quiet of the moonlight
To that voice from the world of men:
Stood thronging the faint moonbeams on the dark stair,
That goes down to the empty hall,
Hearkening in an air stirred and shaken
By the lonely Traveller's call.
And he felt in his heart their strangeness,
Their stillness answering his cry,
While his horse moved, cropping the dark turf,
'Neath the starred and leafy sky;
For he suddenly smote on the door, even
Louder, and lifted his head:
'Tell them I came, and no one answered,
That I kept my word,' he said.
Never the least stir made the listeners,
Though every word he spake
Fell echoing through the shadowiness of the still house
From the one man left awake:
Ay, they heard his foot upon the stirrup,
And the sound of iron on stone,
And how the silence surged softly backward,
When the plunging hoofs were gone.

WALTER DE LA MARE

Flannan Isle

'Though three men dwell on Flannan Isle
To keep the lamp alight,
As we steer'd under the lee, we caught
No glimmer through the night.'

A passing ship at dawn had brought
The news; and quickly we set sail,
To find out what strange thing might ail
The keepers of the deep-sea light.

The winter day broke blue and bright,
With glancing sun and glancing spray,
As o'er the swell our boat made way,
As gallant as a gull in flight.

But, as we near'd the lonely Isle,
And looked up at the naked height;
And saw the lighthouse towering white,
With blinded lantern, that all night
Had never shot a spark
Of comfort through the dark,
So ghostly in the cold sunlight
It seem'd, that we were struck the while
With wonder all too deep for words.

And, as into the tiny creek
We stole beneath the hanging crag,
We saw three queer, black, ugly birds—
Too big, by far, in my belief,
For guillemot or shag—
Like seamen sitting bolt-upright
Upon a half-tide reef:
But, as we near'd, they plunged from sight,
Without a sound, or spurt of white.

And still too mazed to speak,
We landed; and made fast the boat;
And climb'd the track in single file,
Each wishing he was safe afloat,
On any sea, however far,
So it be far from Flannan Isle:
And still we seem'd to climb, and climb,
As though we'd lost all count of time,
And so must climb for evermore.
Yet, all too soon, we reached the door—
The black, sun-blister'd lighthouse-door,
That gaped for us ajar.

As, on the threshold, for a spell,
We paused, we seem'd to breathe the smell
Of limewash and of tar,
Familiar as our daily breath,
As though 'twere some strange scent of death:
And so, yet wondering, side by side,
We stood a moment, still tongue-tied:
And each with black foreboding eyed
The door, ere we should fling it wide,
To leave the sunlight for the gloom:
Till, plucking courage up, at last,
Hard on each other's heels we pass'd
Into the living-room.

Yet, as we crowded through the door,
We only saw a table, spread
For dinner, meat and cheese and bread;
But all untouch'd; and no one there:
As though, when they sat down to eat,
Ere they could even taste,
Alarm had come; and they in haste
Had risen and left the bread and meat:
For at the table-head a chair
Lay tumbled on the floor.
We listen'd; but we only heard
The feeble chirping of a bird

That starved upon its perch:
And, listening still, without a word,
We set about our hopeless search.

We hunted high, we hunted low,
And soon ransack'd the empty house;
Then o'er the Island, to and fro,
We ranged, to listen and to look
In every cranny, cleft or nook
That might have hid a bird or mouse:
But, though we search'd from shore to shore,
We found no sign in any place:
And soon again stood face to face
Before the gaping door:
And stole into the room once more
As frighten'd children steal.

Aye: though we hunted high and low,
And hunted everywhere,
Of the three men's fate we found no trace
Of any kind in any place,
But a door ajar, and an untouch'd meal,
And an overtoppled chair.

And, as we listen'd in the gloom
Of that forsaken living-room—
A chill clutch on our breath—
We thought how ill-chance came to all
Who kept the Flannan Light;
And how the rock had been the death
Of many a likely lad:
How six had come to a sudden end,
And three had gone stark mad:
And one whom we'd all known as friend
Had leapt from the lantern one still night,
And fallen dead by the lighthouse wall:
And long we thought
On the three we sought,
And of what might yet befall.

Like curs a glance has brought to heel,
We listen'd, flinching there:
And look'd, and look'd, on the untouch'd meal
And the overtoppled chair.

We seem'd to stand for an endless while,
Though still no word was said,
Three men alive on Flannan Isle,
Who thought on three men dead.

WILFRID WILSON GIBSON

Hist whist

hist whist
little ghostthings
tip-toe
twinkle-toe

little twitchy
witches and tingling
goblins
hob-a-nob hob-a-nob

little hoppy happy
toad in tweeds
tweeds
little itchy mousies

with scuttling
eyes rustle and run and
hidehidehide
whisk

whisk look out for the old woman
with the wart on her nose
what she'll do to yer
nobody knows

for she knows the devil ooch
the devil ouch
the devil
ach the great

green
dancing
devil
devil

devil
devil

wheeEEE

e. e. cummings

I Like to Stay Up

I like to stay up
and listen
when big people talking
jumbie stories

Ooooooooooooooooooh
I does feel so tingly
and excited
inside—eeeeeeeeeeee

But when my mother say
'Girl, time for bed'
then is when
I does feel a dread
then is when
I does jump into me bed
then is when
I does cover up
from me feet to me head

then is when
I does wish
I didn't listen
to no stupid jumbie story
then is when
I does wish
I did read me book instead

GRACE NICHOLS

Ghosts

That's right. Sit down and talk to me.
What do you want to talk about?

Ghosts. You were saying that you believe in them.
Yes, they exist, without a doubt.

What, bony white nightmares that rattle and glow?
No, just spirits that come and go.

I've never heard such a load of rubbish.
Never mind, one day you'll know.

What makes you so sure?

I said:
What makes you so sure?

Hey,
Where did you go?

KIT WRIGHT

A room bewitched

In the dark, dark wood, there was
  a dark, dark house,
And in that dark, dark house, there was
  a dark, dark room,
And in that dark, dark room, there was
  a dark, dark cupboard,
And in that dark, dark cupboard, there was
  a dark, dark shelf,
And on that dark, dark shelf, there was
  a dark, dark box,
And in that dark, dark box, there was a . . .

ANON.

The Longest Journey in the World

'Last one into bed
has to switch out the light.'
It's just the same every night.
There's a race.
I'm ripping off my trousers and shirt—
he's kicking off his shoes and socks.

'My sleeve's stuck.'
'This button's too big for its button-hole.'
'Have you hidden my pyjamas?'
'Keep your hands off mine.'
If you win
you get where it's safe
before the darkness comes—
but if you lose
if you're last
you know what you've got coming up is
the journey from the light switch
to your bed.
It's the Longest Journey in the World.

'You're last tonight,' my brother says.
And he's right.
There is nowhere so dark
as that room in the moment
after I've switched out the light.

There is nowhere so full of dangerous things—
things that love dark places—
things that breathe only when you breathe
and hold their breath when I hold mine.
So I have to say:
'I'm not scared.'
That face, grinning in the pattern on the wall
isn't a face—
'I'm not scared.'

That prickle on the back of my neck
is only the label on my pyjama jacket—
'I'm not scared.'
That moaning-moaning is nothing
but water in a pipe—
'I'm not scared.'

Everything's going to be just fine
as soon as I get into that bed of mine.
Such a terrible shame
it's always the same
it takes so long
it takes so long
it takes so long
to get there.

From the light switch
to my bed.
It's the Longest Journey in the World.

MICHAEL ROSEN

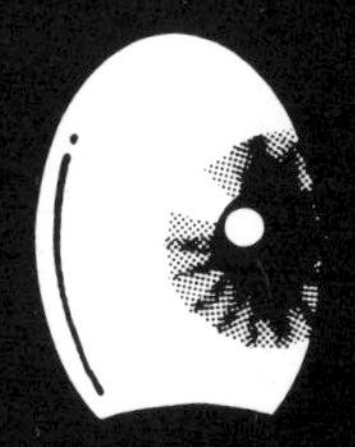
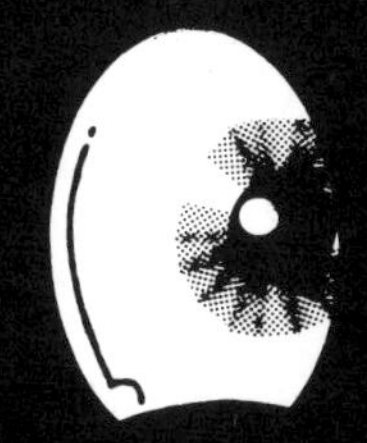

The Hairy Toe

Once there was a woman went out to pick beans,
and she found a Hairy Toe.
She took the Hairy Toe home with her,
and that night, when she went to bed,
the wind began to moan and groan.
Away off in the distance
she seemed to hear a voice crying,
'Where's my Hair-r-ry To-o-oe?
Who's got my Hair-r-ry To-o-oe?'

The woman scrooched down,
'way down under the covers,
and about that time
the wind appeared to hit the house,

smoosh,

and the old house creaked and cracked
like something was trying to get in.
The voice had come nearer,
almost at the door now,
and it said,
'Where's my Hair-r-ry To-o-oe?
Who's got my Hair-r-ry To-o-oe?'

The woman scrooched further down
under the covers
and pulled them tight around her head.

The wind growled around the house
like some big animal
and r-r-um-mbled
over the chimbley.
All at once she heard the door cr-r-a-ack
and Something slipped in
and began to creep over the floor.

The floor went
cre-e-eak, cre-e-eak
at every step that thing took towards her bed.
The woman could almost feel
it bending over her bed.
There in an awful voice it said:
'Where's my Hair-r-ry To-o-oe?
Who's got my Hair-r-ry To-o-oe?
YOU'VE GOT IT!'

ANON.
(*Traditional American*)

Full Moon Rhyme

There's a hare in the moon tonight,
crouching alone in the bright
buttercup field of the moon;
and all the dogs in the world
howl at the hare in the moon.

'I chased that hare to the sky,'
the hungry dogs all cry.
'The hare jumped into the moon
and left me here in the cold.
I chased that hare to the moon.'

'Come down again, mad hare.
We can see you there,'
the dogs all howl to the moon.
'Come down again to the world,
you mad black hare in the moon,

or we will grow wings and fly
up to the star-grassed sky
to hunt you out of the moon,'
the hungry dogs of the world
howl at the hare in the moon.

JUDITH WRIGHT

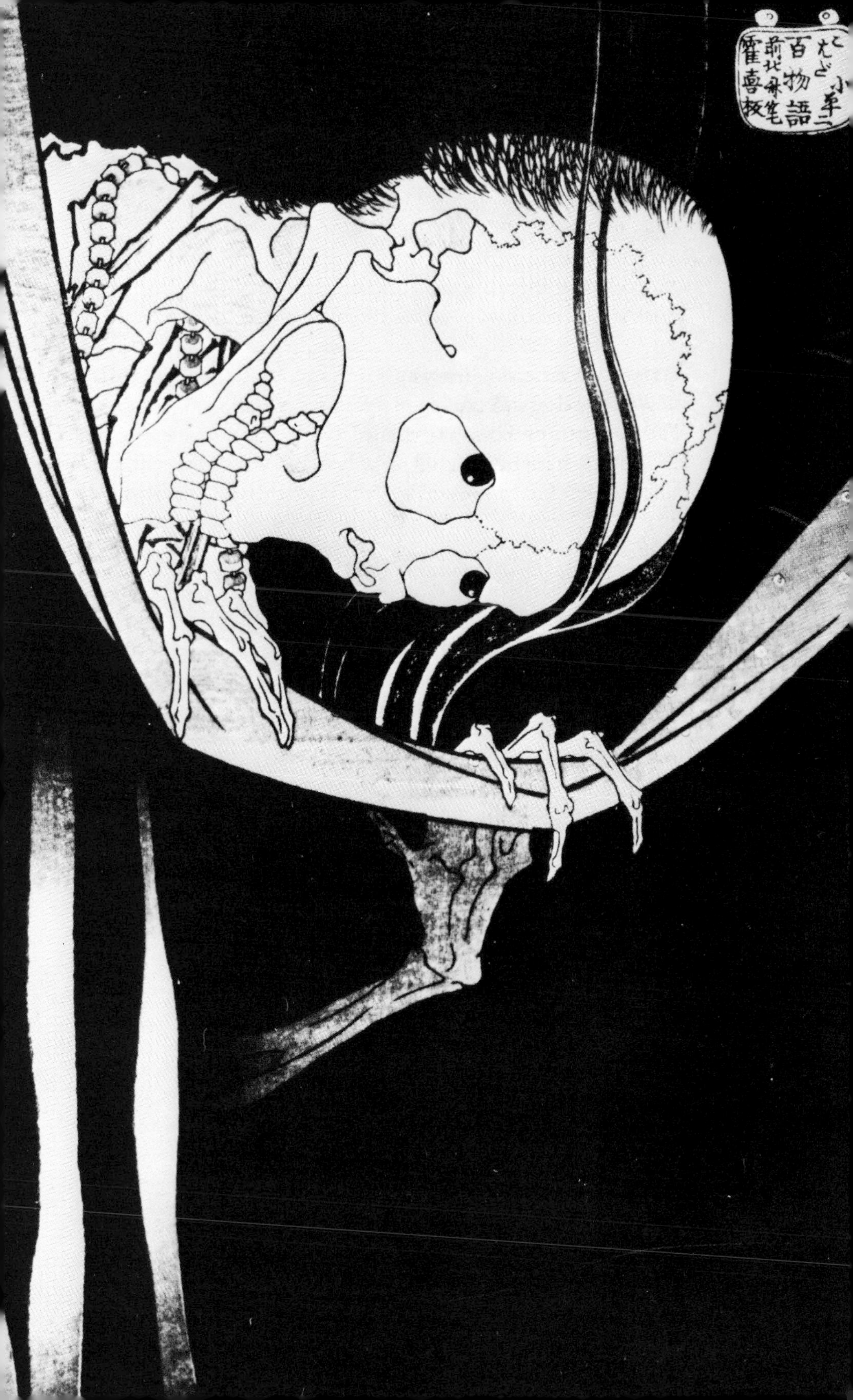
こはだ小平二
百物語
前北斎筆
寉喜板

★ **Chant.** Using Shakespeare's poem from *Macbeth* on p. 181 as a model, write a witches' chant of your own. You might want to work in groups of three! Use Shakespeare's couplet 'Double, double . . .' as your chorus but invent your own horrible ingredients. Try to follow the four-beat rhythm of the lines and the rhyming couplets, if possible. You will need to agree what your menu is for—school dinners? a potion to keep off homework? a magic brew to stop toothache?

★ **Detectives.** Listen to *Flannan Isle* (pp. 185–8) read aloud. Then, as small groups of detectives, re-read and talk about the poem and make a list of the evidence for the disappearance of the three men. Note down any clues, however small, about the position and size of the lighthouse, its history, the time of year, the atmosphere of the place, what the visitors found . . . What do *you* think happened? Each group can present a brief report to the rest of the class, outlining its solution to the mystery. Then hear the poem read aloud again and try to decide whose explanation is the most likely one.

★ **Dramatised readings.** – *Ghosts* (p. 191) is short enough for pairs to learn the lines. Decide who is real and who is the ghost and rehearse the poem, fitting in some simple movements.

– *The Longest Journey in the World* (p. 192) is best performed in groups of three—a narrator and the two brothers. The narrator speaks all the thoughts going through the boy's head and the two brothers share the dialogue. Work out who says which lines carefully. The brothers learn their few lines and fit them to their actions; the narrator reads from the text. Rehearse it through a few times and remember to change the pace from the race at the start to the slow walk across the dark bedroom in the second half of the poem.

★ **Performances.** Many of the poems in this section are good for shared reading aloud:

- *Hist Whist* (p. 189) can be spoken by three voices, alternating solo, duet and trio, to create light, quick, witchy sounds.
- *I Like to Stay Up* (p. 190) is best spoken by a single voice, but sound effects could be added by another.
- *A Room Bewitched* (p. 190) can be shared between two voices taking half a line each, perhaps steadily speeding up towards the last word.

Acknowledgments

The editors and publishers would like to thank the following for their kind permission to reproduce copyright material:

Allan Ahlberg: 'Excuses' from *Please Mrs Butler* (Kestrel Books 1983, page 61) © Allan Ahlberg. Reproduced by kind permission of Penguin Books Ltd.
James Berry: 'Workings of the Wind' from *I Like That Stuff*, Cambridge University Press.
John Betjeman: 'Diary of a Church Mouse' from *Collected Poems*, John Murray (Publishers) Ltd.
Charles Causley: 'What Has Happened to Lulu?', 'John Polruddon', 'A Sailor Sat on the Watery Shore' and 'Tell Me, Tell Me, Sarah Jane' from *Collected Poems*, Macmillan & Co. Ltd, and David Higham Associates.
Richard Church: 'Quiet', 'The Seal' and 'Housing Scheme' from *The Collected Poems of Richard Church*, William Heinemann Ltd.
F. Cornford: 'Childhood' from *Collected Poems*, The Cresset Press.
John Cotton: 'Listen' © John Cotton 1985 from *The Crystal Zoo*: poems by John Cotton, L. J. Anderson and U. A. Fanthorpe (1985) by permission of Oxford University Press.
Adelaide Crapsey: 'Cinquains' from *Verse*, Alfred A. Knopf, Inc., New York, and Algernon S. Crapsey.
Martyn Crucefix: 'George and the Dragon', reprinted by permission of the author.
e. e. cummings: 'maggie and milly and molly and may' and 'hist whist' from *Complete Poems 1913–1962*, Grafton Books (a Division of the Collins Publishing Group).
Clifford Dyment: 'The Tigress' from *Poems 1935–48*, J. M. Dent & Sons Ltd.
T. S. Eliot: 'Prelude I' from *Collected Poems*, and 'The Song of the Jellicles' from *Old Possum's Book of Practical Cats*, Faber & Faber Ltd.
Eleanor Farjeon: 'Mrs Malone' from *Silver Sand and Snow*, Michael Joseph and David Higham Associates (for the Estate of Eleanor Farjeon).
Robert Frost: 'Stopping by the Woods on a Snowy Evening' from *The Complete Poems of Robert Frost*, Jonathan Cape Ltd, and Holt, Rinehart & Winston Inc., New York.
John Fuller: 'Geography Lesson' from *Poets in Hand*.
Andrew Hall: 'A Kingdom of Birds' from *Does it Have to Rhyme*, Fitzjohn's School.
Thomas Hardy: 'Weathers' from *Collected Poems of Thomas Hardy*, Macmillan & Co. Ltd, and the Trustees of the Hardy Estate.
F. W. Harvey: 'Ducks' from *Ducks and Other Poems by F. W. Harvey*, Sidgwick & Jackson Ltd.
John Heath-Stubbs: 'The History of the Flood' from *Selected Poems*, Oxford University Press.
H. G. Henderson (*trans*): 'Bright the Full Moon', 'Summer Night', 'In the House', 'Parting', 'The Little Duck', 'In the Moonlight', 'The Barleyfield', 'Crow', 'The Harvest Moon', 'Haze', 'Spring', 'Heat', 'Dawn', 'Moon Magic', 'Coolness in Summer', and 'Moon Viewing' from *An Introduction to Haiku*, Doubleday & Co. Inc., New York.
Phoebe Hesketh: 'Cornfield' from *The Eighth Day*, Enitharmon Press.
Ralph Hodgson: 'The Bells of Heaven' from *Collected Poems*, Macmillan & Co. Ltd.
Ted Hughes: 'Leaves' from *Season Songs* and 'Mooses' from *Under the North Star*, Faber & Faber Ltd.
T. E. Hulme: 'Above the Dock' and 'Autumn' from *Speculations*, Routledge & Kegan Paul Ltd.
Rudyard Kipling: 'The Way Through the Woods' from *Rewards and Fairies*, Macmillan & Co. Ltd, and Mrs George Bambridge.
James Kirkup: 'The Bird Fancier' and 'The Lonely Scarecrow' from *Refusal to Conform*, Oxford University Press.
D. H. Lawrence: 'Elephants in the Circus', 'Bat', 'Spray', 'Talk' and 'The Rainbow' from *The Complete Poems of D. H. Lawrence*, William Heinemann Ltd.
Roger McGough: 'Two Haiku' from *Waving at Trains*, and 'The Lesson' from *In the Glassroom*, Jonathan Cape Ltd.
Walter de la Mare: 'The Fly', 'The Moth' and 'The Listeners' from *Collected Poems*, The Society of Authors, and the Literary Trustees of Walter de la Mare.
John Masefield: 'Cargoes' and an extract from 'Reynard the Fox', The Society of Authors.
Gerda Mayer: 'May Poem' © Gerda Mayer 1967. Reprinted from *The Candy Floss Tree*: poems by Gerda Mayer, Frank Flynn and Norman Nicholson (1984), by permission of Oxford University Press.
Spike Milligan: 'Soldier Freddy' from *A Dustbin Full of Milligan*, Dennis Dobson, Publishers.
Harold Monro: 'Milk for the Cat', Gerald Duckworth & Co. Ltd.
Ogden Nash: 'Seaside Serenade' and 'Custard the Dragon' from *Family Reunion*, J. M. Dent & Sons Ltd, and Curtis Brown Ltd, New York.
Grace Nichols: 'I Like to Stay Up' from *I Like That Stuff*, Cambridge University Press.
Norman Nicholson: 'Across the Estuary Part I' from *Selected Poems*, Faber & Faber Ltd.
Gareth Owen: 'Out in the City', 'Song of the City', 'The Owl and the Astronaut', 'Thoughts Like an Ocean' and 'Growing Up' from *Song of the City*, Collins Publishers.

Brian Patten: 'Cousin Lesley's See-Through Stomach' and 'Gust Becos I cud not Spel' from *Gargling with Jelly* (Viking Kestrel Books, 1985, pages 16–17, 40–41), copyright © Brian Patten.
Stef Pixner: 'Scarecrow' from *Sawdust and White Spirit* (Virago Press Ltd 1985), copyright © Stef Pixner 1985.
Peter Redgrove: 'At the Edge of the Wood' from *The Nature of Cold Weather and Other Poems*, Routledge & Kegan Paul Ltd.
James Reeves: 'Mr Kartoffel' from *Collected Poems*, William Heinemann Ltd.
W. R. Rodgers: 'The Fountains' from *Awake! and Other Poems*, Martin Secker & Warburg Ltd.
Theodore Roethke: 'The Sloth', 'Mid-Country Blow', 'The Serpent' and 'Child on Top of a Greenhouse' from *Words for the Wind*, Faber and Faber Ltd.
Michael Rosen: 'Go-Kart' and 'Lizzie' from *Quick, Let's Get out of Here*, for 'Tower Block' from *Wouldn't You Like to Know*, and for 'The Longest Journey in the World' from *You Can't Catch Me*, André Deutsch Ltd.
Peggy Seeger and Ewan Macoll: 'The Spring Hill Disaster (Ballad of Spring Hill)', Harmony Music Ltd, and Stormking Music Inc., New York.
Osbert Sitwell: 'Winter the Huntsman', Gerald Duckworth & Co. Ltd.
James Stephens: 'The Main-Deep' from *Collected Poems*, Macmillan & Co. Ltd, and Mrs Iris Wise.
L. A. G. Strong: 'Zeke', 'The Mad Woman' and 'Winter' from *The Body's Imperfection*, Methuen & Co. Ltd.
May Swenson: 'Southbound on the Freeway', first published in *The New Yorker*, © 1963 May Swenson, reprinted by permission of the author.
Edward Thomas: 'Thaw' from *Collected Poems*, and 'Tall Nettles' from *Selected Poems*, Faber & Faber Ltd, and Mrs Myfanwy Thomas.
Arthur Waley: 'Clearing at Dawn' from *Chinese Poems (trans.)*, Allen & Unwin Ltd.
Judith Wright: 'Full Moon Rhyme' from *Selected Poems – Five Senses*, Angus & Robertson (UK) Ltd.
Kit Wright: 'My Dad, Your Dad' and 'Watch Your French' from *Rabbiting On*, Collins Publishers.
W. B. Yeats: 'The Cat and The Moon' from *Collected Poems of W. B. Yeats*, Macmillan and Co. Ltd, and Mr M. B. Yeats.
Andrew Young: 'Last Snow', 'Swallows', 'The Eagle' and 'A Dead Mole' from *Collected Poems*, Rupert Hart- Davis Ltd.

Every effort has been made to trace the copyright holders of the following poems:
Efstathios Georgas: 'The Ballad of Bovver Pete',
Max Endicoff: 'The Excavation',

The authors wish to thank the following for permission to reproduce the illustrations:

Natural History Photographic Agency for the photographs on pages 7 and 92.
The Victoria and Albert Museum for 'The Great Wave' by Hokusai.
Barnaby's Picture Library for the photographs on pages 21, 104 and 176.
The Feofee's of Chetham's Library Manchester and *Mr Neville Cooper* for 'The Ballad Monger'.
Neville Cooper for the photograph on page 34.
Philadelphia Museum of Art for 'Fishes' by Liu Ts'ai.
National Gallery for 'George and the Dragon' by Ucello.
Spectrum Photo Library for the photographs on pages 43, 55, 78 and 84.
Topham Picture Library for the photograph on page 61.
Quentin Blake and *André Deutsch* for the drawings on pages 68–73 and 159–160.
Collection of the *National Palace Museum, Taipei, Taiwan* for 'Cat' by Li Ti.
Tony Stone Photolibrary for the photographs on pages 98–9 and 184.
Salford Corporation and *Mr Neville Cooper* for 'View from the Window of the Royal Technical College, Salford' by L. S. Lowry.
Christine Thwaite and *Penguin Books* for the drawing on page 108.
The Tate Gallery and the *Medici Society Ltd* for 'The Cornfield' by John Nash.
Ashmolean Museum, Oxford for 'Early Morning' by Samuel Palmer.
The British Museum for the drawing on page 114.
Nicholas Bentley and *Faber and Faber* for the drawing on page 123.
John Hillelson Agency Ltd for the photograph on page 144.
Magnum Photos for 'Clown outside Big Top' by Bruce Davidson.